Interactive Homework Workbook

Grade 1

Scott Foresman · Addison Wesley

enVisionMATH™
California

Scott Foresman
is an imprint of

pearsonschool.com

Glenview, Illinois • Boston, Massachusetts • Chandler, Arizona • Shoreview, Minnesota • Upper Saddle River, New Jersey

W9-CTT-933

ISBN – 13: 978-0-328-38441-9

ISBN – 10: 0-328-38441-0

9 10 11 12 VON4 15 14 13 12 11

Contents

Stories About Joining

Join the groups to find how many bugs in all.
Use a counter for each bug. Then count.

2 bugs are on the rock.

1   2

3 bugs are on the blanket.

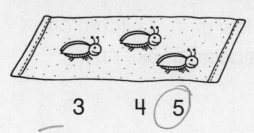

3   4   ⑤

How many bugs are there in all? ___5___ bugs

Tell a joining story for each picture.
Use counters to tell how many in all.

1. 2 birds are in a tree.

2 birds are in a nest.

How many birds are there in all? ___4___ birds

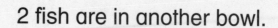

2. 3 fish are in a bowl.

2 fish are in another bowl.

How many fish are there in all? ___5___ fish

Stories About Joining

Solve. Write an addition sentence.

1. 5 children are reading books.
Then 3 more children join them.

   How many children are
   reading books now?

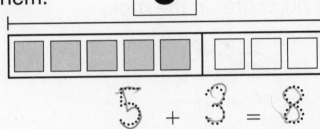

$$5 + 3 = 8$$

2. 7 children are running.
Then 2 more children join them.

   How many children
   are running now?

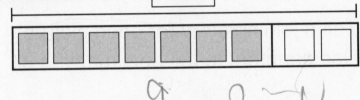

$$9 + 2 = 11$$

3. 3 frogs are in the pond.
Then 3 more frogs join them.

   How many frogs are in the
   pond now?

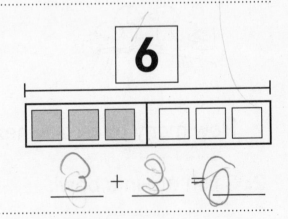

$$3 + 3 = 6$$

Algebra

4. Which number makes the addition sentence true?

   $$5 + \underline{2} = 7$$

1	2	3	6
○	◉	○	○

Problem Solving: Use Objects

You can use objects to help you solve problems.

| | Left | Right |

Bert has 3 pennies.
He put them in 2 pockets.
Use cubes to show the
different ways Bert can do this.

List the different ways.

Right Pocket	0	1	2	3
Left Pocket	3	2	1	0

Use cubes to help you list the different ways.

1. Marlene has 6 grapes.
   She puts them in 2 bowls.

Bowl 1	0	1	2	3	4	5	6
Bowl 2	6	5	4	3	2	1	0

2. Keith has 7 model airplanes.
   He wants to paint some white and some black.

Black	0	1	2	3	4	5	6	7
White	7	6	5	4	3	2	1	0

Problem Solving: Use Objects

Use counters to solve.

1. Lisa puts 8 sweaters into 2 drawers.
   What are 2 different ways she can do this?

2. Jack puts 7 plates on 2 tables.
   What are 2 different ways he can do this?

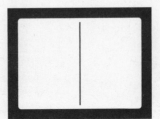 

Number Sense

3. Lynn is planting 9 flowers
   in 2 boxes.
   She plants 6 in the first box.
   Which shows how many she
   plants in the second box?

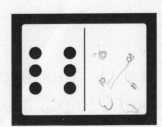

Find Missing Parts of 6 and 7

You can draw a picture to help you
find missing parts of 6 or 7.
Color the part you know.
Count the circles you did not color.
These circles are the missing part.
Write the number.

$2 + \underline{8} = 6$

●●○○○○
Whole

$2 + \underline{4} = 6$

Draw a picture to solve. Write the number.

1. Danielle has 6 toy trucks and cars.
   I toy is a truck.
   How many toys are cars?

   $1 + \underline{5} = 6$

2. There are 7 cats in all.
   Some are black and some are white.
   3 cats are black.
   How many cats are white?

   $3 + \underline{4} = 7$

Reasoning

3. There are 6 ducks in all.
   Some ducks are in the water.
   The same number are in the grass.
   How many ducks are in the grass?

   $\underline{3} + \underline{2} = 6$

Name_____

Finding Missing Parts of 6 and 7

Find the missing part.
Write the numbers.

I.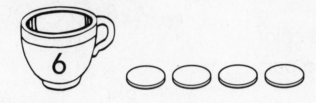

_____   _____   _____
whole   part I know   missing part

2.

_7_   _4_   _____
whole   part I know   missing part

Journal

3. Draw a picture to solve.
Write the number.
There are 7 crackers in all.
Melinda eats 2 crackers.
How many crackers are left
on the plate?

_____ crackers

Find Missing Parts of 8

You can draw a picture
to help you find missing parts of 8.
Color the part you know.
Count the circles you did not color.
These circles are the missing part.
Write the number.

$7 +$ ____ $= 8$

Whole

$7 + 1 = 8$

Draw a picture to solve. Write the number.

1. There are 6 penguins.
   2 penguins are small.
   How many penguins are big?

   $2 +$ _4_ $= 6$

2. Andre has 8 puppies.
   Some puppies are in the house.
   4 puppies are playing in the yard.
   How many puppies are in the house?

   $4 +$ ____ $= 8$

Reasoning

3. Use the picture to solve.
   There are 8 marbles in all.

   _____ marbles are inside.

   _____ marbles are outside.   _____ + _____
   $= 8$

Name_____

Find Missing Parts of 8

Find the missing part.
Write the numbers.

1. There are 8 counters in all.

_____   _____
part I know   missing part

2. There are 8 counters in all.

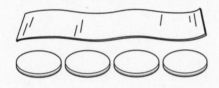

_____   _____
part I know   missing part

Algebra

3. There are 8 books in all.
Which number sentence tells about the picture?

○ $8 - 2 = 6$ ○ $8 - 1 = 7$

○ $8 - 4 = 4$ ○ $8 - 3 = 5$

Find Missing Parts of 9

You can draw a picture
to help you find missing parts of 9.
Color the part you know.
Count the circles you did not color.
These circles are the missing part.
Write the number.

$6 + \underline{\quad} = 9$

Whole

$6 + \underline{3} = 9$

Draw a picture to solve. Write the number.

1. There are 9 horses in the field.
   8 horses are big. The rest are small.
   How many horses are small?

   $8 + \underline{1} = 9$

2. Alexis sees 9 frogs.
   Some frogs are on a log.
   2 frogs are in the grass.
   How many frogs are on the log?

   $2 + \underline{\quad} = 9$

Reasoning

3. Sam has 9 balloons.
   He has 1 more red balloon
   than he has blue balloons.
   Write the number sentence.

   $\underline{\quad} + \underline{\quad} = 9$

Find Missing Parts of 9

1. Find the missing part.
Complete the model.
Then write the numbers.

9

_____   _____

part I know   missing part

---

2. Maria sees 9 boats.
7 boats are in the water.
How many boats are not
in the water?

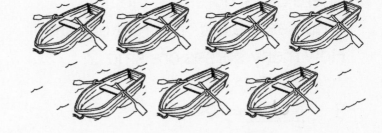

_____ boats

Journal

3. There are 9 apples in all.
Draw some on the tree.
Draw the rest of the apples
on the ground.

Write the numbers.

_____ apples on the tree

_____ apples on the ground

Problem Solving: Use Objects

You can use objects
to show a story and
write a number sentence.

There are 6 hats.
Ashley takes 2 hats.

How many hats are left? __4__
Write the number sentence.

$$6 - 2 = 4$$

Cross out objects to show the story.
Write the number sentence.

I. There are 7 oranges.
Jeff takes 3 oranges.
How many oranges are left?

$$\underline{7} - \underline{} = \underline{}$$

2. There are 5 airplanes.
4 airplanes take off.
How many airplanes
are left?

$$\underline{} - \underline{} = \underline{}$$

Problem Solving: Use Objects

Use counters to show the story.
Write the number sentence.

1. 9 boys are at the park.
5 go home.
How many boys are left?

$$9 - 5 = 4$$

____ – ____ = ____

2. 6 ducks are in the pond.
3 fly away.
How many ducks are left?

____ – ____ = ____

3. There are 8 books on
the shelf.
Dana takes 2 books.
How many books are left?

____ – ____ = ____

4. There are 4 pears.
Emily eats 1.
How many pears are left?

____ – ____ = ____

5. 7 bees are in the garden.
5 fly away.
How many bees are left?

____ – ____ = ____

6. There are 3 block towers.
2 get knocked over.
How many towers are left?

____ – ____ = ____

Number Sense

7. You have 5 buttons.
Which is the greatest number of
buttons you can give away?

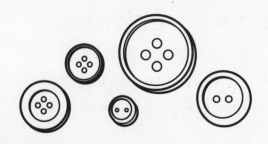

○ 6   ○ 3

○ 5   ○ 1

Representing Numbers on a Ten-Frame

You can use a ten-frame
to show numbers up to 10.

To show 3, start at the top left box.
Count as you draw a counter for
each number.

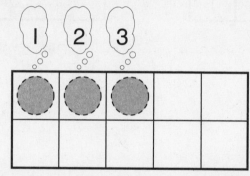

Draw counters in the ten-frame
to show each number.

1. 6

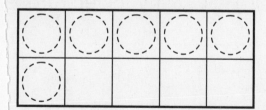

2. 8

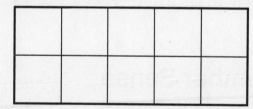

3. 7

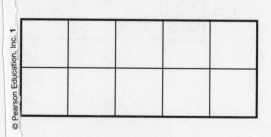

4. 9

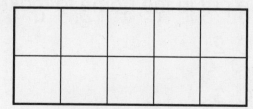

Representing Numbers on a Ten-Frame

Draw counters in the ten-frame to show each number.

1. $\boxed{4}$

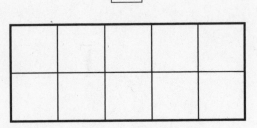

2. $\boxed{6}$

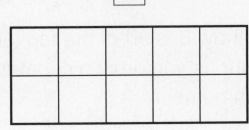

Algebra

Draw counters.

3. Show how 7 is 5 and 2.

4. Show how 9 is 5 and 4.

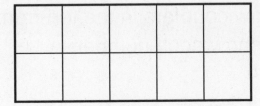

Number Sense

5. Kyle put 6 counters in a ten-frame. How many more counters should Kyle put in the frame to make 10?

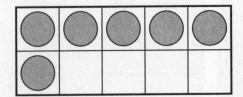

○ 2   ○ 4

○ 3   ○ 5

Recognizing Numbers on a Ten-Frame

A ten-frame is made up of 2 five-frames. So, you can use what you learned about five-frames to help you read numbers on a ten-frame.

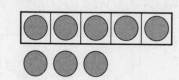

For example, the number 8 on a five-frame and a ten-frame looks very much alike.

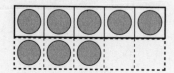

5 and 3 is 8.

Write the number shown on each ten-frame.

1. _____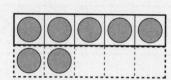

2. _____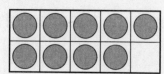

Spatial Thinking

Draw the counters. Then write the number.

3. Jim uses a ten-frame to show 5 and 5 more.

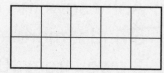

4. Bernice wrote about the ten-frame. Circle what Bernice wrote.

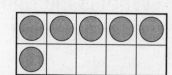

5 and 5 is 10.   4 away from 10 is 6.   5 and 2 is 7.

Recognizing Numbers on a Ten-Frame

Write the number shown on each ten-frame.

1.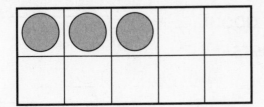

_____

2.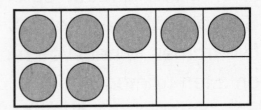

_____

Spatial Thinking

Draw the counters. Then write the number.

3. Rob uses a ten-frame.
   He shows 5 and 3 more.
   What number does he show?

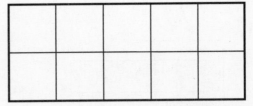

_____

Number Sense

Draw the counters. Then solve the problem.

4. Abby says the ten-frame shows
   5 and 2 more. Jake says it shows
   3 away from 10.
   What is the number in
   the ten-frame?

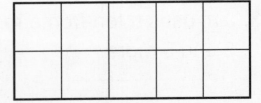

7	5	3	2
○	○	○	○

Name_____

Parts of 10

Here are some different ways to make 10.

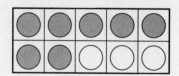

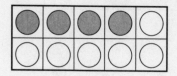

7 and 3   4 and 6

Write the numbers that show ways to make 10.

1.

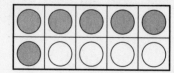

_____6_____ and _____4_____

2.

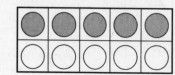

_____ and _____

3.

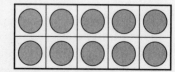

_____ and _____

4.

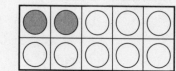

_____ and _____

5.

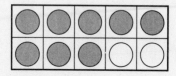

_____ and _____

6.

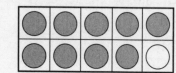

_____ and _____

Parts of 10

Write the numbers that show ways to make 10.

1.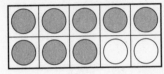

10 is _____ 8 _____ and _____ 2 _____

2.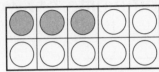

10 is _____ and _____

3.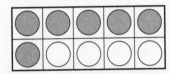

10 is _____ and _____

4.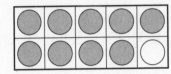

10 is _____ and _____

5.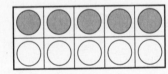

10 is _____ and _____

6.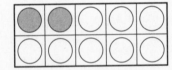

10 is _____ and _____

Number Sense

7. Which numbers are parts of 10?

    ○ 4 and 5   ○ 7 and 3

    ○ 1 and 8   ○ 9 and 2

Finding Missing Parts of 10

You can use a ten-frame
to help you find missing parts of 10.

Draw the counters from
the model in a ten-frame.
This is the part you know.

To find the missing part,
draw more counters to fill the frame.

Write the numbers.

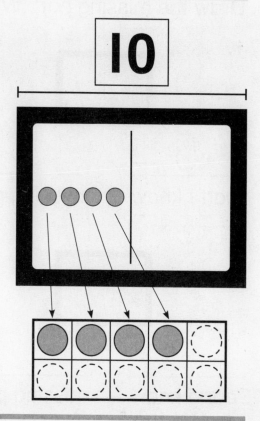

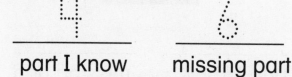

4	6
part I know	missing part

Look at the model.
Draw the missing part in the ten-frame.
Write the numbers.

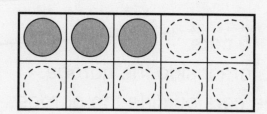

_____   _____
part I know   missing part

Finding Missing Parts of 10

Draw the missing part. Write the numbers.

1.

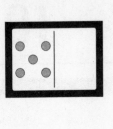

____5____   ____5____
part I know   missing part

2.

_____   _____
part I know   missing part

3.

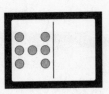

_____   _____
part I know   missing part

4.

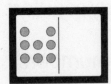

_____   _____
part I know   missing part

Algebra

Write the missing part.

5. $4 + \_\_\_\_ = 10$

6. $1 + \_\_\_\_ = 10$

Journal

Draw a picture to solve the problem.

7. There are 10 cars.
   Some cars are inside the garage.
   Draw some cars outside the garage.
   Write the parts.

_____   _____
part I know   missing part

Problem Solving:
Make a Table

Katrina has purple marbles and yellow marbles.
She can only fit 5 marbles in her pocket.
How many different ways can Katrina put
5 marbles in her pocket?

To solve the problem, you need to
find how many different ways Katrina
can put the marbles in her pocket.

You can make a table
and then count how
many ways you made.

1. Complete the table.

2. There are _____ different ways.

3. What is the sum of each row
in your table?

_____

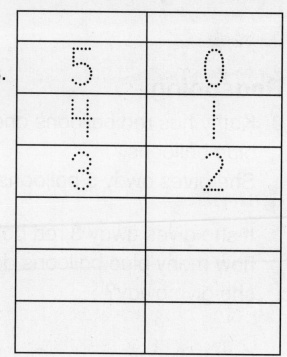

5	0
4	1
3	2

Problem Solving:
Make a Table

Make a table to solve the problem.

Strawberries	Grapes
0	
	3
6	

I. Ed eats 6 pieces of fruit.
He can eat strawberries or grapes.

Show the ways Ed could pick which fruit to eat.

_____ ways

2. If Ed eats 4 strawberries,
how many grapes does he eat?

_____

Reasoning

Red	Blue

3. Kathy has red balloons and
blue balloons.
She gives away 5 balloons.

If she gives away 3 red balloons,
how many blue balloons does
she give away?

○ 3 balloons   ○ I balloon

○ 2 balloons   ○ 0 balloons

Thinking Addition with Doubles

Doubles help you to subtract.

Think: $3 + 3 =$ __6__   so $6 - 3 =$ __3__

Add the doubles.
Then use the doubles to help you subtract.

1.

$1 + 1 =$ __2__   so $2 - 1 =$ _____

2.

$4 + 4 =$ _____   so $8 - 4 =$ _____

Visual Thinking

Complete the addition and subtraction sentences.

3. $2 + 2 =$ _____

$4 - 2 =$ _____

Thinking Addition with Doubles

Add the doubles.

Then use the doubles to help you subtract.

1.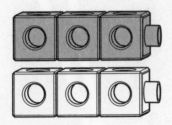

$$\begin{array}{r} 3 \\ + 3 \\ \hline 6 \end{array}$$
$$\begin{array}{r} 6 \\ - 3 \\ \hline 3 \end{array}$$

If 3 + 3 = 6,

then 6 − 3 = 3.

2.

$$\begin{array}{r} 4 \\ + 4 \\ \hline \end{array}$$
$$\begin{array}{r} 8 \\ - 4 \\ \hline \end{array}$$

3.

$$\begin{array}{r} 6 \\ + 6 \\ \hline \end{array}$$
$$\begin{array}{r} 12 \\ - 6 \\ \hline \end{array}$$

4.

$$\begin{array}{r} 2 \\ + 2 \\ \hline \end{array}$$
$$\begin{array}{r} 4 \\ - 2 \\ \hline \end{array}$$

5.

$$\begin{array}{r} 5 \\ + 5 \\ \hline \end{array}$$
$$\begin{array}{r} 10 \\ - 5 \\ \hline \end{array}$$

Number Sense

6. Mark the double that will help you subtract.

8 − 4 = _____

○ 3 + 3   ○ 5 + 5

○ 4 + 4   ○ 8 + 8

Thinking Addition to 8

You can think addition to help you subtract.

Think: I know
2 + 6 = 8,
so 8 – 6 = 2

$$\underline{2} + \underline{6} = \underline{8}$$

$$\underline{8} - \underline{6} = \underline{2}$$

Write an addition fact. Think of the addition fact to help you write and solve the subtraction fact.

1.

$$\underline{2} + \underline{4} = \underline{6}$$

$$\underline{6} - \underline{4} = \underline{2}$$

2.

$$\underline{} + \underline{} = \underline{7}$$

$$\underline{7} - \underline{} = \underline{}$$

3.

$$\underline{} + \underline{} = \underline{}$$

$$\underline{} - \underline{} = \underline{}$$

4.

$$\underline{} + \underline{} = \underline{}$$

$$\underline{} - \underline{} = \underline{}$$

Algebra

5. If $\triangle + \bigcirc = \square$, then

$$\underline{} - \underline{} = \underline{}$$

Thinking Addition to 8

Think addition to help you subtract.

1.

Think 4 + _____ = 6

so 6 − 4 = _____

2.
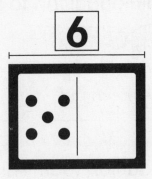

Think 5 + _____ = 6

so 6 − 5 = _____

3.

Think 5 + _____ = 8

so 8 − 5 = _____

4.

Think 4 + _____ = 7

so 7 − 4 = _____

Algebra

5. Tia needs to make 8 baskets. She makes 2 baskets.
How many more baskets does Tia need to make?
Which addition fact can help you subtract?

○ 8 + 6 = 14

○ 2 + 8 = 10

○ 6 + 6 = 12

○ 2 + 6 = 8

Thinking Addition to 12

You can use addition facts to help you subtract.

$8 + 1 = 9$

$9 - 1 = 8$

$8 + 1 = 9$
and
$9 - 1 = 8$
are related facts.

Use the addition fact to help you subtract.

1.

$10 - 2 =$ _____

$8 + 2 = 10$

2.

$11 - 4 =$ _____

$7 + 4 = 11$

3.

$12 - 9 =$ _____

$3 + 9 = 12$

4.

$11 - 6 =$ _____

$5 + 6 = 11$

Thinking Addition to 12

Think addition to help you subtract.

1.

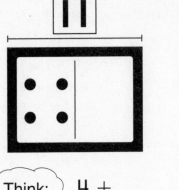

Think: $4 + \underline{\hspace{1cm}} = 11$

so $11 - 4 = \underline{\hspace{1cm}}$

2.

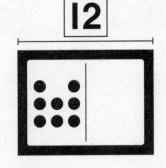

Think: $8 + \underline{\hspace{1cm}} = 12$

so $12 - 8 = \underline{\hspace{1cm}}$

3.

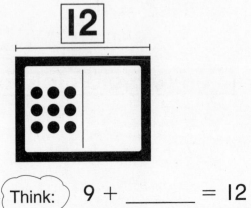

Think: $9 + \underline{\hspace{1cm}} = 12$

so $12 - 9 = \underline{\hspace{1cm}}$

4.

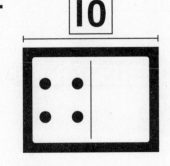

Think: $4 + \underline{\hspace{1cm}} = 10$

so $10 - 4 = \underline{\hspace{1cm}}$

Problem Solving

5. Mark scores 6 points. Amy scores 11 points.
How many points does Mark need to tie the game?
Write a number sentence to solve.

$\underline{\hspace{1.5cm}} \bigcirc \underline{\hspace{1.5cm}} = \underline{\hspace{1.5cm}}$

$\underline{\hspace{1.5cm}}$ points

Problem Solving: Draw a Picture and Write a Number Sentence

You can draw a picture to help you solve a problem.

Mia has 7 grapes.
First, draw a picture of all the grapes.

Mia eats 3 grapes.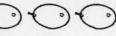
Cross out the grapes she eats.

Count how many grapes are left. _____4_____ grapes

Write a number sentence that tells about the picture.

__7__ − __3__ = __4__

Check your work.
Does the number sentence match the picture?

Read the problem. Draw a picture.
Then write a number sentence.

1. Jonah has 9 baseballs.
   Sara has 4 baseballs.
   How many more baseballs
   does Jonah have than Sara?

   _____ − _____ = _____

Problem Solving: Draw a Picture and Write a Number Sentence

Write a subtraction sentence to solve.
Draw a picture to check.

I. Abby has 8 apples.
She gives away 3 apples.
How many apples does
she have left?

8 _____ – _____ = _____

2. Maya has 9 pears.
3 pears are green.
The rest are yellow.
How many pears are yellow?

_____ – _____ = _____

Reasoning

3. There are 7 birds. 3 birds fly away.
How many birds are left?
Which number sentence can
help you find the answer?

○ 7 – 2 = 5   ○ 9 – 7 = 2

○ 7 – 3 = 4   ○ 7 – 6 = 1

Problem Solving:
Make an Organized List

You can use pattern blocks to make another shap

How many can fit in ? <u>2</u>

How many can fit in 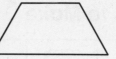 ? <u>3</u>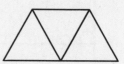

There are 3 ways you can make
this shape using pattern blocks.

Complete the organized list.

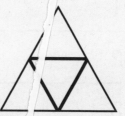

Ways to Make			
	△	▱	⬭
Way 1	4	0	0
Way 2			
Way 3			

Problem Solving:
Make an Organized List

How many ways can you make
this shape using pattern blocks?

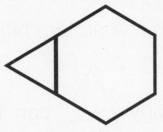

1. Make a list.

Ways to Make 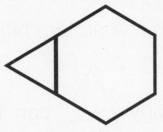	⬡ trapezoid	⬡ hexagon	△ triangle	▱ rhombus
Way 1				
Way 2				
Way 3				
Way 4				
Way 5				
Way 6				

Journal

2. How many ways can you use pattern blocks
to make a ▱ ? Explain.

Sorting Solid Figures

You can sort solid figures in many ways.
Some figures can go into more than one group.

Some figures have flat
surfaces (faces).

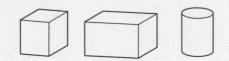

Some have curved surfaces
and can roll.

Some have vertices (corners).

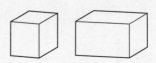

Some have no vertices.

Circle the figure that follows the sorting rule.

1. It has all flat surfaces.

2. It has no flat surfaces.

3. It can roll.

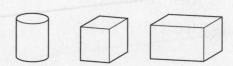

4. Circle the 2 figures
that have flat surfaces
and curves.

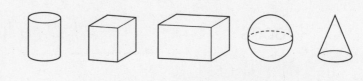

Sorting Solid Figures

Read the sorting rule.
Circle 1, 2, or 3 solid figures that follow the rule.

1. 1 face

2. 8 vertices

3. 2 faces

4. 6 faces

5. 0 vertices

Algebra

6. Mark the rule that tells how these solid figures are alike.

 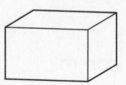

○ 3 vertices   ○ 5 vertices

○ 4 faces   ○ 6 faces

Making New Shapes from Shapes

Give 3 ways you can make this shape using pattern blocks.

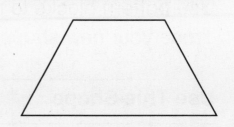

You need to find all the ways that pattern blocks can make the shape.

A list can help you keep track.

Ways to Make ⏢			
Shapes I Used	⏢	△	▱
Way 1	1	0	0
Way 2	0	3	0
Way 3	0	1	1

Did you find 3 ways? How do you know?

Give 3 ways you can make this shape using pattern blocks. Complete the list.

I.

Ways to Make ▱			
Shapes I Used	⏢	▱	△
Way 1	1	0	1
Way 2			
Way 3			

Making New Shapes from Shapes

Use pattern blocks to make each shape.
Trace your new shape.

Use This Shape	Make This Shape	Trace New Shape
1. △	⬡	
2. △	▱	
3. △	⏢	

....

Journal

4. Use pattern blocks to make a new shape.
Draw the blocks you used below.

Location of Shapes

Where is the ?

behind **in front of** **above** **below** **left** **right**

Circle where the is.

1.

behind

(in front of)

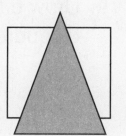

2.

left

right

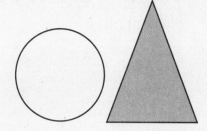

3.

in front of

above

left

4.

above

behind

below

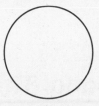

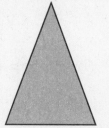

Location of Shapes

1. Draw a rectangle in front of a circle.

2. Draw a triangle above a rectangle.

3. Draw a square behind a circle.

4. Draw a triangle below a square.

Spatial Thinking

5. Where is the cone?

○ to the right of the cylinder

○ above the cylinder

○ to the left of the cube

○ behind the cube

Name_____

Location on a Grid

This is a map of Felipe's town.
You want to go from the school to Felipe's house.

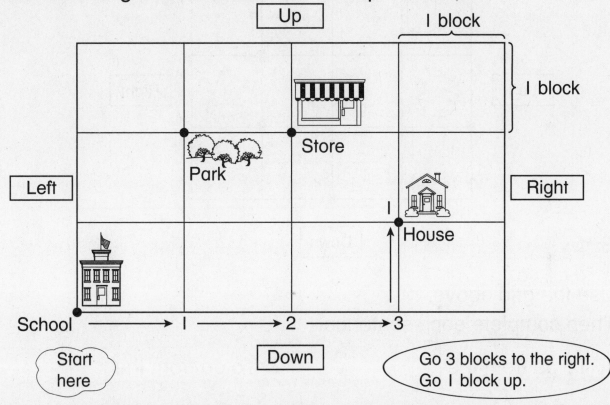

Read the map. Then complete each sentence.

1. To go from the 🏫 to the 🌳🌳🌳,

go __1__ block right and __2__ blocks up.

2. To go from the 🏠 to the 🏪,

go _____ block left and _____ block up.

3. To go from the 🏠 to the 🌳🌳🌳,

go _____ blocks left and _____ block up.

Name_____

Location on a Grid

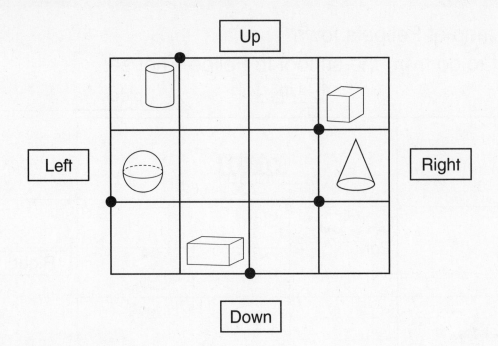

Up

Left

Right

Down

Use the grid above.

Then complete each sentence.

1. To go from the

to the , go

_____ spaces right

and _____ spaces down.

2. To go from the

to the , go

_____ spaces left

and _____ space up.

Spatial Thinking

3. Which shape is 1 space down
and 3 spaces left from the ?

 ○

 ○

○

○

100

Describing Patterns

This is a pattern.

  repeats over and over.

This is a pattern too.

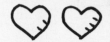

 repeats over and over.

Circle the pattern unit.

1.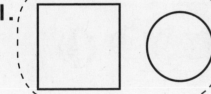

2.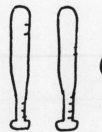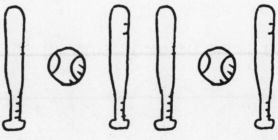

3.

Name_____

Describing Patterns

Circle the pattern unit.

1.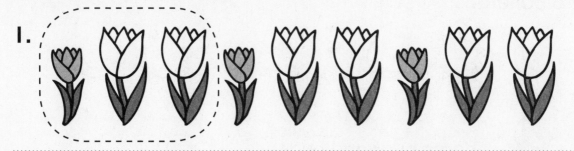

2.

3.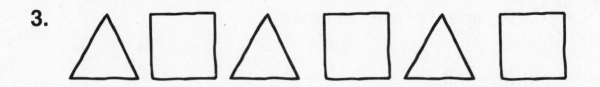

4.

Journal

5. Make the same pattern using other shapes or letters.

Name_____

Using Patterns to Predict

The stripes make a pattern.
What color should the white stripe be?

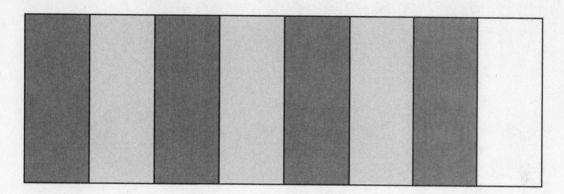

Find the pattern.
Color what is missing.

1.

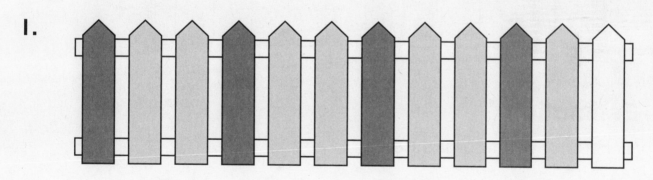

2.

Using Patterns to Predict

Find the pattern.
Color what is missing.

1.

2.

3.

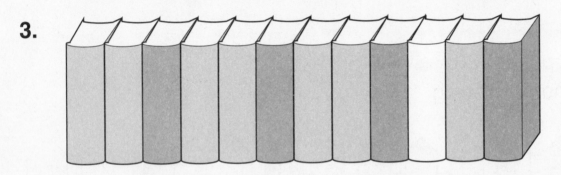

Estimation

4. Predict what comes next.

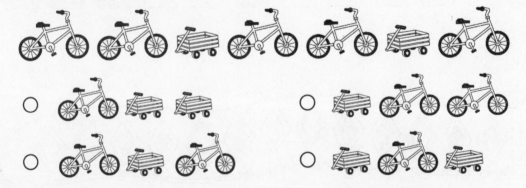

Extending Shape Patterns

Look at these patterns.

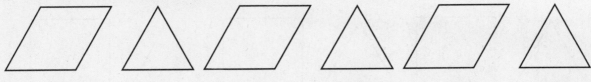

A   B   A   B   A   B

repeats over and over. A B repeats over and over.

Use pattern blocks. Make a pattern. Draw the pattern.
Then make the same pattern using letters.

1.

A   B   A   B   A   B
___   ___   ___   ___   ___   ___

2.

S T
___ ___ ___ ___ ___ ___ ___ ___

Reasoning

3. Draw a picture that shows the part that repeats.

Extending Shape Patterns

Look at the pattern.
Make the same pattern using letters.

1.

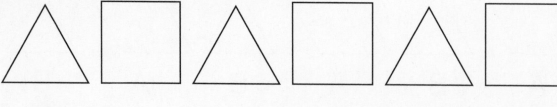

A ___ ___ ___ ___ ___ ___

2.

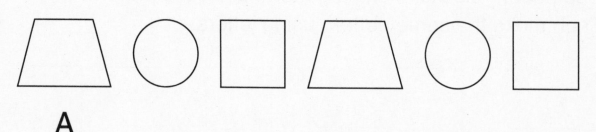

A ___ ___ ___ ___ ___ ___

Reasoning

3. Draw a picture that shows the part that repeats.

Problem Solving:
Look for a Pattern

A pattern can be anything that repeats.
It can be colors, shapes, numbers, letters,
or objects.
To find a pattern, look for what repeats.

Write what comes next. ____B____

1. Zoë drew a pattern.

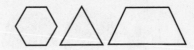

Draw what comes next. ________

Algebra

2. Use these shapes to make a pattern.

3. Use these numbers to make a pattern.

Problem Solving:
Look for a Pattern

Write, draw, or color to complete the pattern.

1. △ ◯ ▢ ▢ △ ◯ ▢ _____ _____ _____

2. A D C A D C _____ _____ _____

3.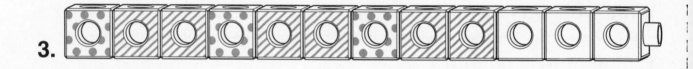

4. 2 4 6 2 4 6 _____ _____ _____

Visual Thinking

5. Which ball is missing?

Estimating and Ordering Lengths of Time

About how long does each activity take?
You can estimate to find the answer.

(I minute)   I minute   I minute
I hour   (I hour)   I hour
I day   I day   (I day)

About how long does each activity take?
Circle your estimate.

1.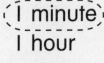

     about I minute
     (about I hour)
Do homework.   about I day

2.

     about I minute
     about I hour
Wash hands.   about I day

3.

     about I minute
     about I hour
Build a doghouse.   about I day

4.

     about I minute
     about I hour
Play a game.   about I day

Estimating and Ordering Lengths of Time

About how long does each activity take?
Mark your estimate.

1.

○ about 1 minute   ○ about 1 day

○ about 1 hour   ○ about 2 days

2.

○ about 2 minutes   ○ about 1 day

○ about 2 hours   ○ about 2 days

....

Reasoning

3. Jon wakes up in the morning
and gets ready for school.
He gets dressed, brushes his teeth,
and eats breakfast.

Put Jon's activities in order
from the longest to the shortest.

_____   _____   _____

longest   shortest

Problem Solving:
Use Data from a Table

Nature Center Schedule	
Activity	**Time**
Hike	9:00
Feed Turtles	10:00
Pick Flowers	11:00
Bird Watch	12:00

A schedule tells the time at which activities start.

Look for the activity.

The hike starts at ⋯9:00⋯.

Look at the time.

At 12:00 we ⋯Bird Watch⋯.

Use the schedule to answer the questions. Circle your answer.

I. Which activity comes just before feeding the turtles?

Bird Watch   Hike   Pick Flowers

2. Which activity comes just after picking flowers?

Hike   Feed Turtles   Bird Watch

3. At what time does the activity Pick Flowers begin?

9:00   10:00   11:00

4. Which activity starts at 10:00?

Hike   Feed Turtles   Bird Watch

117

Problem Solving:
Use Data from a Table

Use the schedule to answer the questions.

Time	Activity	
9:00		Art
9:30		Tee-Ball
10:00		Music
10:30		Puppet Theater
11:00		Swimming

1. What activity is at 9:00? _____

2. What activity is just
before Music? _____

3. What activity is just after
Puppet Theater? _____

Reasoning

4. At what time does Music begin?

9:00	9:30	10:00	10:30
○	○	○	○

Name_____

Numbers Made with Tens

You can count the models to find out
how many groups of ten.

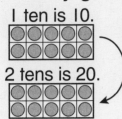

1 ten is 10.

2 tens is 20.

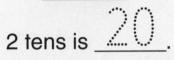

1 ten is 10.

2 tens is 20.

3 tens is 30.

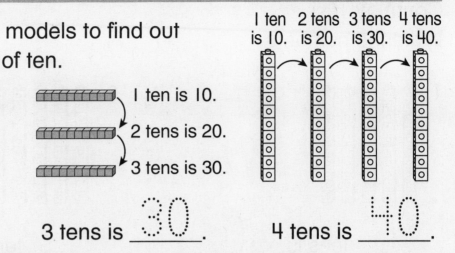

1 ten   2 tens   3 tens   4 tens
is 10.   is 20.   is 30.   is 40.

2 tens is _20_.   3 tens is _30_.   4 tens is _40_.

Count the models. Write how many. Then write the number.

1.

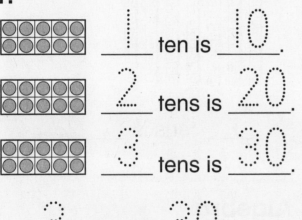

_1_ ten is _10_.

_2_ tens is _20_.

_3_ tens is _30_.

_3_ tens is _30_.

2.

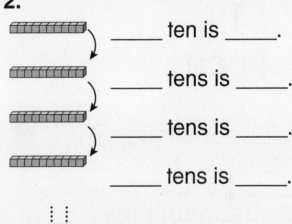

____ ten is ____.

____ tens is ____.

____ tens is ____.

____ tens is ____.

_4_ tens is ____.

3.

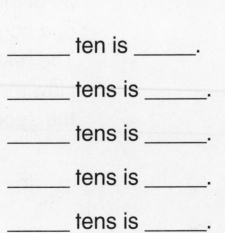

_____ ten is _____.

_____ tens is _____.

_____ tens is _____.

_____ tens is _____.

_____ tens is _____.

_____ tens is _____.

Numbers Made with Tens

Count by 10s.
Write the numbers.

1.

__5__ tens is __50__.

2.

_____ tens is _____.

3.

_____ tens is _____.

4.

_____ tens is _____.

Reasonableness

5. Which number is shown?

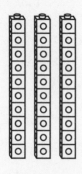

○ 3   ○ 12

○ 10   ○ 30

Algebra

6. Nancy has 50 marbles.
30 of the marbles are in one bag.
The rest are in another bag.
How many marbles are in the second bag?

○ 40   ○ 20

○ 30   ○ 10

Tens and Ones on a Hundred Chart

Start at 6. Count by tens on the hundred chart.

1	2	3	4	5	6	7	8	9	10
11	12	13	14	15	16	17	18	19	20
21	22	23	24	25	26	27	28	29	30
31	32	33	34	35	36	37	38	39	40
41	42	43	44	45	46	47	48	49	50
51	52	53	54	55	56	57	58	59	60
61	62	63	64	65	66	67	68	69	70
71	72	73	74	75	76	77	78	79	80
81	82	83	84	85	86	87	88	89	90
91	92	93	94	95	96	97	98	99	100

When you count by tens from a number, the ones digits in the numbers you say are the same as the number you start from. The tens digit of each of the next numbers is 1 more than the last tens digit.

6, 16 , 26 , 36 , 46 , 56 , 66 , 76 , 86 , 96

1. Count by tens.
Circle the ones digit that does not change in each number.

3, _____ , _____ , _____ , _____ , _____ , _____ , _____ , _____ , _____

2. Count by tens.
Draw arrows to show how the tens digits go up by 1 in each number.

8, _____ , _____ , _____ , _____ , _____ , _____ , _____ , _____ , _____

Tens and Ones on a Hundred Chart

1. Color the numbers you say when
you start at 9 and count by 10s.

1	2	3	4	5	6	7	8	9	10
11	12	13	14	15	16	17	18	19	20
21	22	23	24	25	26	27	28	29	30
31	32	33	34	35	36	37	38	39	40
41	42	43	44	45	46	47	48	49	50
51	52	53	54	55	56	57	58	59	60
61	62	63	64	65	66	67	68	69	20
71	72	73	74	75	76	77	78	79	80
81	82	83	84	85	86	87	88	89	90
91	92	93	94	95	96	97	98	99	100

2. Start at 1. Count by tens.
Write the numbers.
Use the hundred chart to help.

1, ____ , ____ , ____ , ____ , ____ , ____ , ____ , ____ , ____

Number Sense

3. Kyra is counting by tens from 5.
Which numbers does she miss?

5, 15, ____ , 35, ____ , 55, 65, ____ , 85, 95

○ 25, 45, 75   ○ 25, 40, 75

○ 20, 40, 70   ○ 20, 45, 70

Problem Solving:
Make an Organized List

How many ways can you show 18 with tens and ones?

How many tens are in 18? __1__

How many ones are left over? __8__

Tens	Ones
1	8
0	18

Break apart a ten into 10 ones.

How many ones are there? __18__

Make a list to show the ways.

1. Olivia wants to show 25 with tens and ones.
Make a list to show the ways.

Tens	Ones
2	5

Reasonableness

2. Penny says there are 4 ways to make 26.
Is she correct?

Yes   No

Name_____

Problem Solving:
Make an Organized List

Use cubes and make a list to solve.

1. Kelly shows all the ways to make 49 as tens and ones. What ways does she show?

Tens	Ones

2. Marc wants to show 34 as tens and ones. What are all the ways he can show?

Tens	Ones

Reasoning

3. Hector's list shows ways to make 52, but he forgot 1 way. Which numbers are missing from his list?

○ 5 and 12   ○ 4 and 12

○ 4 and 22   ○ 3 and 12

Tens	Ones
5	2
3	22
2	32
1	42
0	52

Number Line Estimation

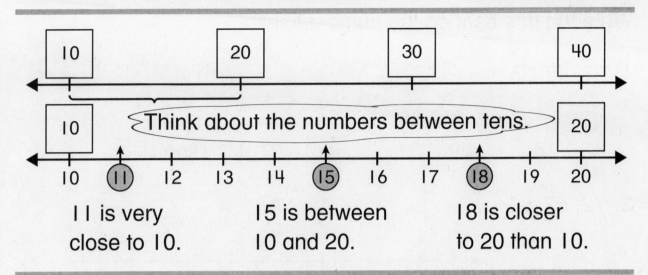

| 10 | 20 | 30 | 40 |

| 10 | Think about the numbers between tens. | 20 |

10   11   12   13   14   15   16   17   18   19   20

11 is very   15 is between   18 is closer
close to 10.   10 and 20.   to 20 than 10.

Count by 10s to complete the number line.
Then draw lines to show where the numbers go.

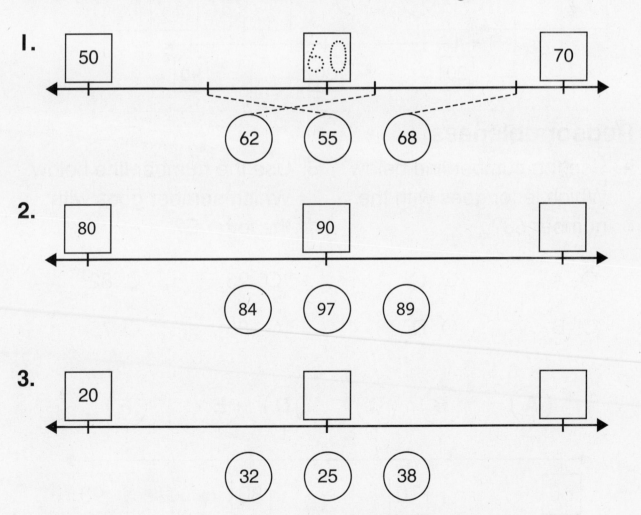

1.

| 50 | 60 | 70 |

(62)   (55)   (68)

2.

| 80 | 90 | |

(84)   (97)   (89)

3.

| 20 | | |

(32)   (25)   (38)

Number Line Estimation

Write the numbers on the number line.

1. 31, 48, 36

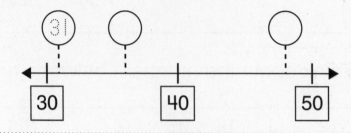

2. 72, 63, 59

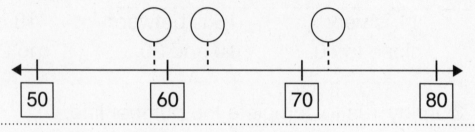

3. 28, 23, 37

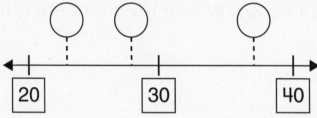

Reasonableness

4. Use the number line below. Which letter goes with the number 68?

   ○ A   ○ C

   ○ B   ○ D

5. Use the number line below. Which number goes with the letter E?

   ○ 95   ○ 82

   ○ 85   ○ 75

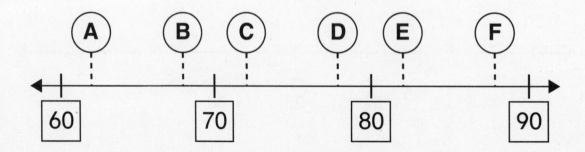

Ordinals to Tenth

You can use ordinal numbers to tell you the position of people or things that are in order. You can write an ordinal number for any whole number.

1st   2nd   3rd   4th   5th   6th   7th   8th   9th   10th

This girl is 1st in line.

This boy is sixth in line. There are 5 children in front of him.

Look at the picture.

1st

1. Circle the 1st object.

2. Cross out the 6th object.

3. What position is the fish? _____

4. What is in the 5th position? _____

5. How many things are before the kite? _____

Ordinals to Tenth

Circle the word that completes each sentence.

1. Banji lives on the _____ floor.

   second   third   fourth

2. Calvin lives on the _____ floor.

   sixth   seventh   eighth

3. Samir lives on the _____ floor.

   third   fourth   fifth

4. Nan lives on the _____ floor.

   eigth   ninth   tenth

Andre 🔲 🖼
🔲 🔲 Nan 🖼
🖼 Erek 🔲
Li 🔲 🖼 🔲
🔲 🔲 Calvin 🖼
Samir 🖼 🔲
🔲 🖼 Agatha
🔲 Banji 🔲 🖼
🖼 🔲 Lyn 🔲
First
1st Tom 🖼 🔲

Spatial Reasoning

5. Hank has a sheep with curved horns.
   His sheep did not come in eighth place.
   What place did Hank's sheep get at the fair?

   ○ 1st place   ○ 8th place

   ○ 3rd place   ○ 10th place

Making Reasonable Estimates

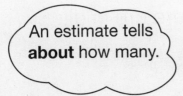

An estimate tells **about** how many.

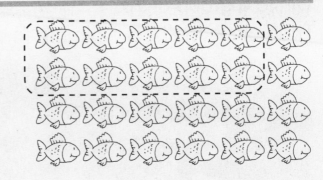

Circle 10 fish.
About how many more groups
of 10 fish do you see?

There are about   10   (20)   30   fish in all.

Circle a group of 10. Then circle the best estimate
for how many there are in all.

1.

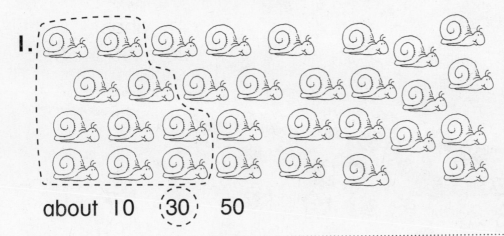

about   10   (30)   50

2.

about   10   20   30

Making Reasonable Estimates

Circle a group of 10.
Then circle the best estimate for how many there are in all.

1.

about
20 (50) 70

2.

about
20   40   60

3.

about
10   30   50

4. Estimation Tammy estimates that
she has about 30 stamps.
Which number could show
how many stamps Tammy really has?

○ 3   ○ 32

○ 21   ○ 43

164

Problem Solving:
Make an Organized List

Kyla picks a number card.
Her number is less than 40.
It is greater than 35.
Which number does she pick?

Make a list to find Kyla's number.

Look at the first clue.
List the numbers in the box
that are less than 40.

29
32
38

Kyla's number could be 29, 32, or 38.

Look at the second clue.
Circle the numbers on the list
that are greater than 35.
38 is greater than 35.

29
32
38

Kyla's number must be 38.

I. Ian picks a number card.
His number is even.
It is less than 60.
What number does Ian pick?

Make a list of the even number cards.
Then circle the number on the list
that is less than 60.

_____

_____

Ian's number must be _____.

Problem Solving:
Make an Organized List

Make a list. Write the color of the motorcycle.

| red | pink | orange | yellow | green | blue | purple | black |

1st   8th

1. This motorcycle is between the 3rd motorcycle and the 6th motorcycle.

Which color could it be?

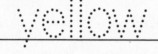

_____

This motorcycle is the color of the sun. What color is the motorcycle?

_____

2. This motorcycle is between the 1st motorcycle and the 4th motorcycle.

Which color could it be?

_____

_____

This motorcycle is the color of a pumpkin. What color is the motorcycle?

_____

....

Reasoning

Make a list to find the secret number.

3. I am a number greater than 55.
I am in a square.
Which number am I?

  ○ 28   ○ 60

  ○ 63   ○ 78

Name_____

Making 10 to Add 8

You can make 10 to find 8 + 6.
Draw 8 white marbles and 6 black marbles.

Circle a group of 10. Count the leftover marbles.
Then complete the number sentence.

10 + ___4___ = 14, so 8 + 6 = ___14___

Circle a group of 10. Then write 2 addition sentences.

1. Kim has 8 white toy bears.
Tia has 4 gray toy bears.
How many bears do they
have in all?

10 + _____ = 12, so 8 + 4 = _____

---

2. Tamika caught 8 butterflies.
Cecil caught 7 butterflies.
How many butterflies
were caught altogether?

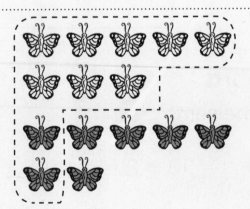

10 + _____ = _____, so 8 + 7 = _____

Name_____

Making 10 to Add 8

Draw counters to help you add.
Write the missing addend.
Then write the sums.

1.

8
$+$ 6
―――
?

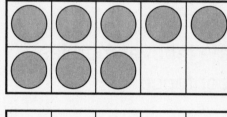

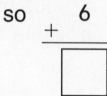

10   8
$+\boxed{}$ so $+$ 6
―――   ―――
$\boxed{}$ $\boxed{}$

2.

8
$+$ 3
―――
?

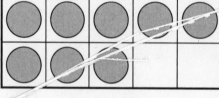

10   8
$+\boxed{}$ so $+$ 3
―――   ―――
$\boxed{}$ $\boxed{}$

Algebra

Find the sum.

3. $8 + 4 = 10 + 2 = $ _____

11   12   13   14
○   ○   ○   ○

Problem Solving:
Two-Question Problems

Jill has 6 marbles. She gets 5 more. $6 + 5 = \underline{11}$ marbles
How many marbles does
she have in all?

I know Jill has 11 marbles in all.
I know she gives Sal 8.
I can subtract to find how many
she has left.

Jill gives 8 marbles to Sal.
Now how many marbles
does Jill have?

$11 - 8 = \underline{3}$ Jill has $\underline{3}$ marbles left.

1. Jack has 4 model cars. He gets 3 more model cars.
   How many model cars does Jack have in all?

   $\underline{4} + \underline{3} = \underline{7}$ model cars

   For his birthday Jack gets 5 model cars.
   How many model cars does he have now?

   _____ + _____ = _____ model cars

2. Nicky has 6 charms on her bracelet. She buys 8 **more**.
   How many charms does Nicky have in all?

   _____ + _____ = _____ charms

   On the way home 4 charms are lost.
   How many charms does Nicky have now?

   _____ − _____ = _____ charms

Problem Solving:
Two-Question Problems

Write number sentences to solve both parts.

1. Peter read 7 books about dinosaurs.
   He read 8 books about sharks.
   How many books did Peter read in all?

   _____ ◯ _____ = _____ books

   Peter did not like 6 of the books he read.
   How many books did Peter like?

   _____ ◯ _____ = _____ books

Journal

Write a second problem to go with the first problem.
Solve your problem.

2. Nate counts dogs at the dog park.
   He sees 9 small dogs and 7 big dogs.
   How many dogs does he see in all?

   $9 + 7 = 16$

   _____

   _____

   _____

   _____

Problem Solving: Draw a Picture and Write a Number Sentence

You can write a number sentence to solve problems.

Avi played 2 games of basketball.
He scored 8 points in the first game.
He scored 6 points in the second game.
How many points did Avi score in all?

You can draw a picture to help you solve the problem.
Then you can write a number sentence.

$$8 + 6 = 14$$

Complete the model.
Then write a number sentence.

1. Gina has 9 books.
She buys 4 more books.
How many books
does Gina have now?

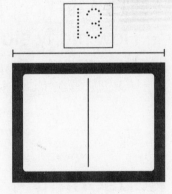

___ ⊕ ___ = 13

2. Metta sees 15 frogs.
7 frogs hop away.
How many frogs
are left?

___ ◯ ___ = ___

Problem Solving: Draw a Picture and Write a Number Sentence

Write a number sentence to solve.
Draw a picture to check your answer.

1. Helen made invitations for her party.
   She made 7 invitations on Monday.
   She made 6 invitations on Tuesday.
   How many invitations
   did Helen make in all?

   _____ ◯ _____ = _____ invitations

2. Joe started at the bottom
   of the stairs.
   He hopped up 9 stairs.
   Then he hopped down 3 stairs.
   How many stairs is Joe
   from the bottom?

   _____ ◯ _____ = _____ stairs

Reasoning

3. Which number sentence
   tells how many apples in all?

   ○ 8 − 7 = 1   ○ 7 + 1 = 8

   ○ 8 − 1 = 7   ○ 7 + 8 = 15

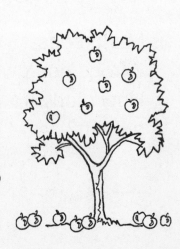

Practicing Addition Facts

$$\begin{array}{r} 6 \\ + 5 \\ \hline \end{array}$$

6 and 5 are 1 apart. They are near doubles.

$$\begin{array}{r} 6 \\ + 6 \\ \hline 12 \end{array}$$

$$\begin{array}{r} 6 \\ + 5 \\ \hline 11 \end{array}$$

$$\begin{array}{r} 9 \\ + 5 \\ \hline \end{array}$$

9 is close to 10. I can make 10.

$$\begin{array}{r} 9 \\ + 5 \\ \hline 14 \end{array}$$

$$\begin{array}{r} 10 \\ + 4 \\ \hline 14 \end{array}$$

Add. Then circle the strategy you used.

1.
$$\begin{array}{r} 5 \\ + 4 \\ \hline 9 \end{array}$$

Doubles

┌ ─ ─ ─ ─ ─ ─ ─ ─ ─ ┐
Near Doubles
└ ─ ─ ─ ─ ─ ─ ─ ─ ─ ┘

Make 10

Think: 5 and 4 are 1 apart. They are near doubles.

2.
$$\begin{array}{r} 7 \\ + 7 \\ \hline \end{array}$$

Doubles

Near Doubles

Make 10

Think: 7 and 7 are doubles.

3.
$$\begin{array}{r} 8 \\ + 3 \\ \hline \end{array}$$

Doubles

Near Doubles

Make 10

Think: 8 is close to 10.

Practicing Addition Facts

Find each sum.

1. 9
  + 3
  12

2. 7
  + 7

3. 5
  + 6

4. 4
  + 9

5. 9
  + 5

6. 7
  + 8

7. 6
  + 6

8. 7
  + 4

Journal

9. Write a story problem that can be solved by making 10. Then explain how to solve the problem.

_____

_____

_____

_____

_____

Problem Solving: Use Objects

Sarah picked 9 flowers.
Then she picked 5 more.

You can use counters to model the addition. Then you can complete the story.

How many flowers did she pick in all? __14__

These counters are the 9 flowers Sarah picked.

These counters are the 5 flowers Sarah picked.

Put the counters together. Sarah picked 14 flowers.

$9 + 5 = $ __14__

Use counters to model the addition.
Complete the story.

1. $6 + 6 = 12$

Malik ate __6__ crackers.

Then he ate _____ more crackers.

How many crackers did Malik eat in all? _____

Problem Solving: Use Objects

Write a story or draw a picture for each number sentence.

1. $12 - 5 = 7$

....

2. $13 - 8 = 5$

....

3. $7 + 9 = 16$

....

Number Sense

4. Which number sentence
matches the story and drawing?
Hoshi caught 5 fish.
Then Hoshi caught 6 more fish.
She caught 11 fish in all.

    ○ $6 - 5 = 1$ ○ $5 + 5 = 10$

    ○ $11 - 6 = 5$ ○ $5 + 6 = 11$

Using Data from Real Graphs

You can use real objects
to make a graph by arranging
the objects in rows and columns.

This is a real-object graph because the counters are real objects.

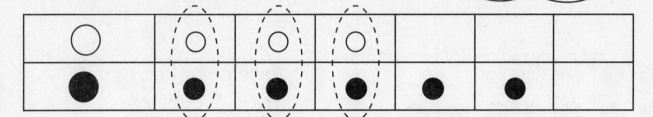

Circle each pair of counters in the graph.

Is there the same number of colors?   yes   no

Which color has more?   black   white

How many counters do not have a partner? ___2___

I. Circle the correct answers. Write the number.

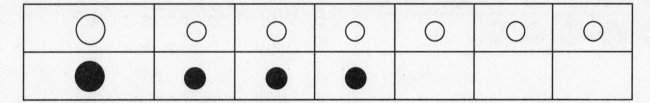

Is there the same number of colors?   yes   no

Which color has more?   black   white

How many counters do not have a partner? _____

Using Data from Real Graphs

Look at the graph.
Circle the correct answers. Write the number.

1. Is there the same number of colored counters?
yes   no

2. Which color has more?
gray   black

3. How many counters do not have a partner?

_____

4. Is there the same number of colored counters?
yes   no

5. Which color has more?
gray   black

6. How many counters do not have a partner? _____

Journal

7. Draw black counters on the graph so 1 black counter does not have a partner.

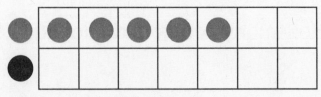

Problem Solving:
Making a Graph

Each square that is colored gray equals 1 child's selection.

Name of
Fairy-Tale
Characters

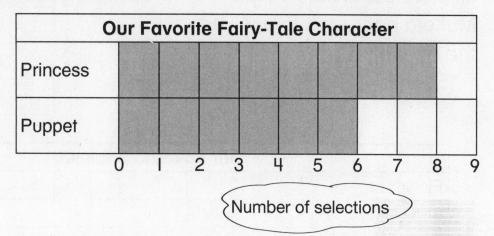

Our Favorite Fairy-Tale Character									
Princess									
Puppet									

0   1   2   3   4   5   6   7   8   9

Number of selections

Look at the number of squares colored for the princess.

How many squares are colored? ___8___

Look at the number of squares colored for the puppet.

How many squares are colored? ___6___

Circle the favorite fairy-tale character of the children.

Princess   Puppet

1. Ask your classmates to select their favorite snack.
Color to make a bar graph. Then answer the questions.

Yogurt									
Fruit									

0   1   2   3   4   5   6   7   8   9

2. Which snack is the favorite? _____

3. How many children selected fruit? _____

Problem Solving:
Making a Graph

The chart shows what kinds of
stickers the children like.
Make a bar graph to answer
the questions.

Favorite Stickers		
🖼	Flower	2
🖼	Bird	4
🖼	Boat	7
🖼	Dog	3

Our Favorite Stickers

	0	1	2	3	4	5	6	7	8
Flower									
Bird									
Boat									
Dog									

1. Which sticker do children like the most? _____

2. Which sticker do children like the least? _____

Number Sense

3. Which of the following shows the stickers in order from
most favorite to least favorite?

   ○ dog, boat, bird, flower   ○ flower, bird, boat, dog

   ○ flower, dog, bird, boat   ○ boat, bird, dog, flower

Name_____

Values of Penny and Nickel

A nickel = 5 cents.
Skip count by 5s for nickels.

A penny = 1 cent.
Count by 1s for pennies.

Skip count by 5s for the nickels.
Then count on by 1s for the pennies.

5 ¢ → 10 ¢ → 15 ¢ → 16 ¢ → 17 ¢ → 18 ¢

In All
18 ¢

Skip count by 5s and count on by 1s to find
how much money in all.

1.

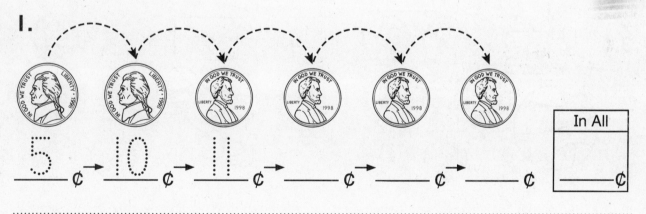

5 ¢ → 10 ¢ → 11 ¢ → ___ ¢ → ___ ¢ → ___ ¢

In All
___ ¢

2.

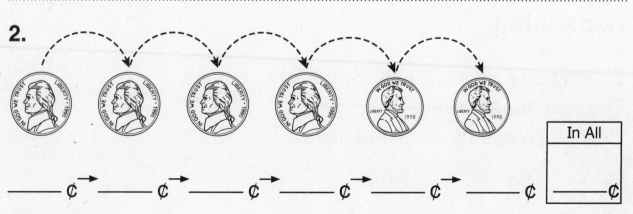

___ ¢ → ___ ¢ → ___ ¢ → ___ ¢ → ___ ¢ → ___ ¢

In All
___ ¢

Values of Penny and Nickel

I. Count on. Then write how much money in all.

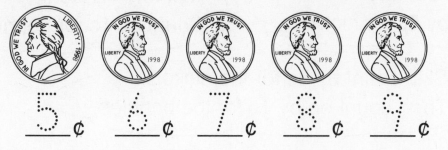

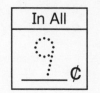

5̲_¢   6̲_¢   7̲_¢   8̲_¢   9̲_¢ | In All 9̲_¢ |

2.

____¢   ____¢   ____¢   ____¢   ____¢ | In All ____¢ |

Circle the coins that match each price.

3.

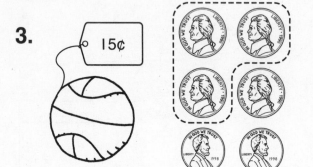

4.

Reasoning

5. Jan has 6 coins. She has 2 nickels.
The rest are pennies.
How much money does Jan have?

15¢   14¢   13¢   12¢
○   ○   ○   ○

Value of Half-Dollar

Here are some ways to show 50¢.

half-dollar coin

50̣̣¢

2 quarters

2̣5̣¢ → 5̣0̣¢

4 dimes and 2 nickels

1̣0̣¢ → 2̣0̣¢ → 3̣0̣¢ → 4̣0̣¢ → 4̣5̣¢ → 5̣0̣¢

In All
5̣0̣¢

Circle the group of coins that makes 50¢.

1.

2.

Value of Half-Dollar

Circle the coins that equal 50¢.

1.

2.

3.

Reasoning

4. Max has 50¢ in all.
2 coins are dimes.
Which are his other coins?

○

○

○

○

Counting Sets of Coins

Count the coins.
Start with the coin that is worth the most money.

Remember > stands
for "greater than."

50¢ 75¢ 85¢ 90¢ 91¢

In All
91 ¢

Skip count. Then write how much money in all.

I.

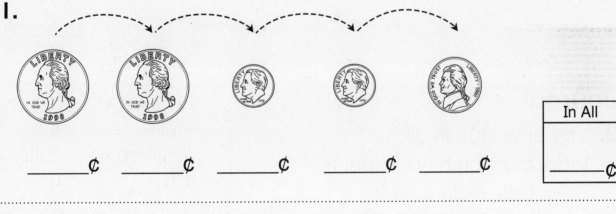

____¢ ____¢ ____¢ ____¢ ____¢

In All
____¢

2.

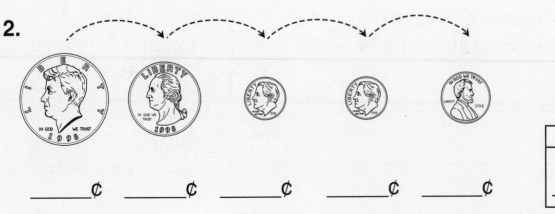

____¢ ____¢ ____¢ ____¢ ____¢

In All
____¢

Counting Sets of Coins

Skip count. Then write how much money in all.

1.

_____¢ _____¢ _____¢ _____¢ _____¢

In All
_____¢

2.

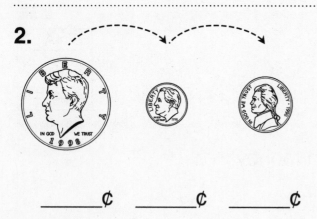

_____¢ _____¢ _____¢

In All
_____¢

Journal

3. You have 50¢ in all.
What can you buy for lunch?
Be sure to include fruit.
How much will it cost?
How much will you have left?

_____

_____

Problem Solving:
Try, Check, and Revise

Jim bought 2 toys at the toy fair. Together they cost 11¢.
Which toys did he buy?

Pick two toys. Find their total.

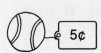

Try 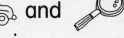 and  .

Add. ____6____ ¢ + ____8____ ¢ = ____14____ ¢

14¢ is more than 11¢.

Find a toy that costs less than 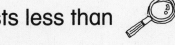 .

The ⬤ costs less.

Try the and ⬤ .

Add. ____6____ ¢ + ____5____ ¢ = ____11____ ¢

Jim bought the and ⬤ .

___

1. Circle the 2 toys that cost 15¢.

 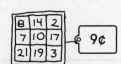

_____ ¢ + _____ ¢ = _____ ¢

 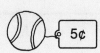

Name_____

Problem Solving:
Try, Check, and Revise

Circle the stickers each child bought.
Write an addition sentence to check.

   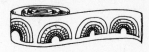

   4¢   5¢   8¢   9¢

1. Venus bought 2 different stickers.
Together they cost 14¢.
What did Venus buy?

5̈_____¢ + _____¢ = _____¢

2. Kevin bought 2 different stickers.
Together they cost 17¢.
What did Kevin buy?

_____¢ + _____¢ = _____¢

Number Sense

3. Carlos bought 2 different stickers.
Together they cost 9¢.
Which did Carlos buy?

○     ○

○     ○

230

Comparing and Ordering by Length

You can compare and order objects by how long they are.

Line up the objects.

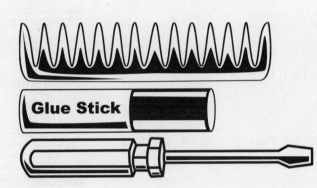

Look to see which object is longest and which is shortest.

Then put the objects in order from longest to shortest.

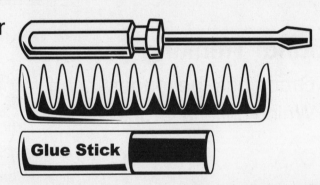

1. Complete the sentence.

Line A _____

Line B _____

Line C _____

Line _____ is the longest.   Line _____ is the shortest.

Reasoning

2. Use the clues to color the scarves.

The shortest scarf is red.
The green scarf is longer
than the blue scarf.

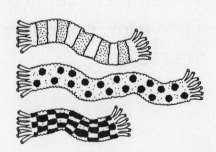

Comparing and Ordering by Length

Draw lines to match the object with the word that describes it.

1. longest

shortest

2. longest

shortest

Spatial Thinking

3. Grace has the longest scarf.
Which child is Grace?

○ A   ○ C

○ B   ○ D

A   B   C   D

Reasoning

4. Use the clues to color the cars.

The shortest car is green.
The yellow car is longer than
the red car.

Name_____

Using Units to Estimate and Measure Length

Look at the paper clip.

Look at the string.

Estimate: How many paper clips long is the string?

About ___4___ paper clips long.

Now measure.

> Be sure you put the paper clips right next to each other.

> Be sure all paper clips are the same size.

> Line up the first paper clip with the edge of the string.

Measure: About ___3___ paper clips long.

That is close to the estimate.

Estimate. Then measure using paper clips.

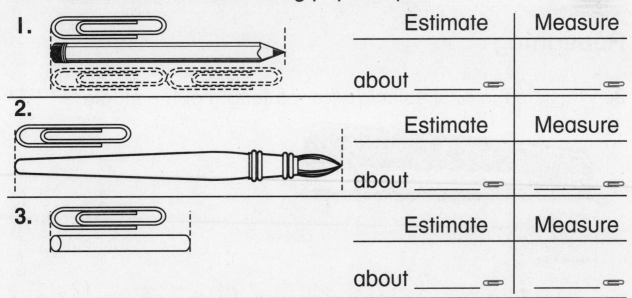

	Estimate	Measure
1. about _____		

	Estimate	Measure
2. about _____		

	Estimate	Measure
3. about _____		

Name_____

Using Units to Estimate and Measure Length

Estimate the length. Then use cubes to measure.

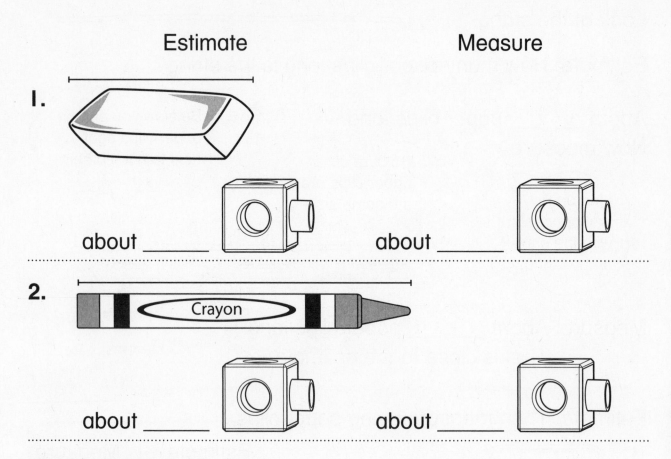

Estimate	Measure

1.

about _____

about _____

2.

about _____

about _____

Reasoning

3. Which is the best estimate for the length of the stapler?

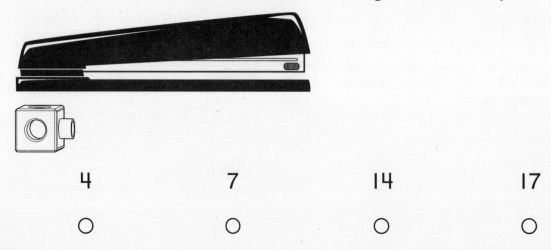

4	7	14	17
○	○	○	○

Unit Size and Measuring

Predict: Will you need more chalk or
more paper clips to measure the marker?

more 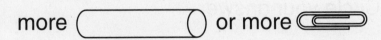 or more

You must find out if you need more chalk or more paper clips.

Use reasoning to help you.
The paper clip is shorter.
You will probably need more paper clips.

Measure to check.

more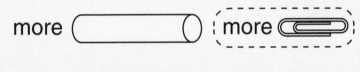

Measure to check your prediction.
Was your prediction correct?

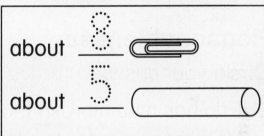

about ___8___

about ___5___

I. Will it take fewer pieces of chalk or fewer paper clips
to measure the stapler?
Circle your prediction. Then measure.

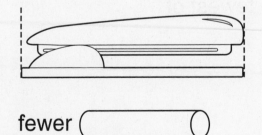

fewer

fewer

Measure to check.

about _____

about _____

Name_____

Unit Size and Measuring

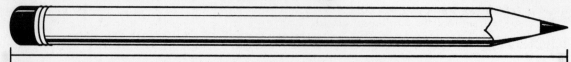

1. Will you need more cubes or more paper clips
to measure the pencil? Circle your answer.

more

more

2. Measure the length of the pencil.

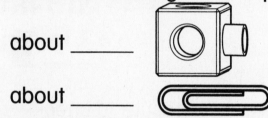

about _____

about _____

Reasonableness

Circle your answer.

3. Eric has a paintbrush that is about 12 cubes long.
How many paper clips long could it be?

2    7    12

Spatial Thinking

4. Which object would you need the fewest of
to measure how long the eraser is?

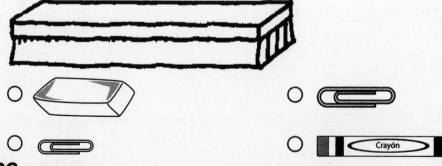

○   ○

○   ○ Crayón

Name_____

Comparing and Ordering by Volume

Here are 3 objects.
Which object takes up the least space?
Which object takes up the most space?

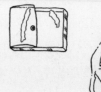

Look at each object.

Would it fit into a large box or a small box?

I need a small box for the pencil and a larger box for the backpack.

Compare the objects. Then order them.

least space   most space

Draw the objects in order from the one that takes the most space to the one that takes the least space.

1.

most space   least space

2.

most space   least space

Name_____

Comparing and Ordering by Volume

Circle the object that takes up the least space.

1.

2.

3.

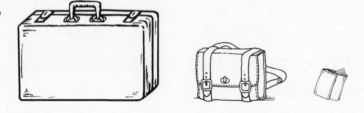

Reasoning

4. The red pillow takes the least space.
The yellow pillow takes more space than the
blue pillow. Which of the following is not true?

○ The red pillow takes
more space than the
blue pillow.

○ The yellow pillow takes
more space than the
red pillow.

○ The blue pillow takes
more space than the
red pillow.

○ The red pillow takes
less space than the
yellow pillow.

238

Name_____

Comparing and Ordering by Weight

Weight is the measure of how heavy or light an object is.
You can compare objects by weight.

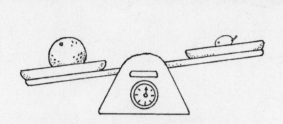

| The orange is heavier than the grape. | The pineapple is heavier than the orange. |

After you compare the objects, you can order them by weight.

heaviest   lightest

I. Draw lines to match the object with the word that describes it.

heaviest - - -

lightest

Estimation

2. Circle the fruits that weigh about the same amount.

Comparing and Ordering by Weight

Circle the object that is the heaviest.

1.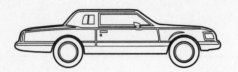

....

Circle the object that is the lightest.

2.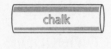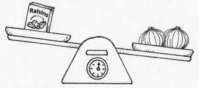

....

Spatial Thinking

Use the pictures to answer the questions.

3. Which object is the heaviest? **4.** Which object is the lightest?

_____   _____

....

5. Which list shows the vegetables in order from heaviest to lightest?

○ squash, peas, tomato   ○ tomato, squash, peas

○ peas, tomato, squash   ○ squash, tomato, peas

240

Problem Solving:
Use Reasoning

The tool you choose to measure an object depends on what you want to measure.

Clive wants to measure his fishbowl.

How tall is it?	How heavy is it?	How much does it hold?

Use paper clips to measure length.	Use a pan balance to measure weight.	Use a cup to measure capacity.

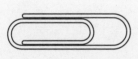 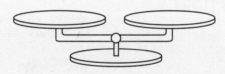 

Circle the tool Clive should choose to measure how much water the fishbowl will hold.

Circle the best tool to use for each measurement.

1. How heavy is it?

 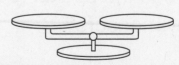 

2. How tall is it?

 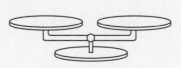 

Problem Solving:
Use Reasoning

Circle the best tool to use for the measurement.

1. How long is it?

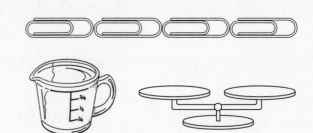

2. How heavy is it?

3. How much does it hold?

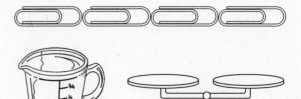

Reasoning

4. Oliver and Ben have a bucket.
They want to use the bucket to measure.
What can they measure?

   ○ capacity   ○ area

   ○ weight   ○ length

Name_____

Adding Groups of 10

You can use what you know about adding ones
to add groups of ten.

2 ones and 5 ones are 7 ones.   2 tens and 5 tens are 7 tens.

  2 + 5 = 7   20 + 50 = 70

Write each number sentence.

1.

$\underline{3} + \underline{2} = \underline{5}$ $\underline{30} + \underline{20} = \underline{50}$

2.

$\underline{} + \underline{} = \underline{6}$ $\underline{} + \underline{} = \underline{60}$

3.

$\underline{} + \underline{} = \underline{}$ $\underline{} + \underline{} = \underline{}$

4.

$\underline{} + \underline{} = \underline{}$

5.

$\underline{} + \underline{} = \underline{}$

Adding Groups of 10

Write numbers to complete each number sentence.

1.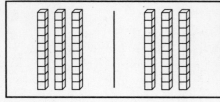

_____ tens + _____ tens = _____ tens

_____ + _____ = _____

Complete each number sentence.

2. 50 + 20 = _____   **3.** 30 + 40 = _____

4. 20 + 30 = _____   **5.** 70 + 20 = _____

6. 60 + 30 = _____   **7.** 10 + 80 = _____

Number Sense

8. David has 2 books of stamps.
The first book has 50 stamps.
The other book has 30 stamps.
How many stamps does David have in all?

○ 20   ○ 80

○ 70   ○ 90

Adding Tens on a Hundred Chart

1	2	3	4	5	6	7	8	9	10
11	12	13	14	15	16	17	18	19	20
21	22	23	24	25	26	27	28	29	30
31	32	33	34	35	36	37	38	39	40
41	42	43	44	45	46	47	48	49	50
51	52	53	54	55	56	57	58	59	60
61	62	63	64	65	66	67	68	69	70
71	72	73	74	75	76	77	78	79	80
81	82	83	84	85	86	87	88	89	90
91	92	93	94	95	96	97	98	99	100

When you add tens on a hundred chart, you skip count by tens. The ones digit in each number is the same as the ones digit in the number you started from.

The tens digit of each number is one more than the tens digit of the number before it.

Use the hundred chart to add tens to 16.

1.   16
      + 10
      ──────
      26

2.   16
      + 20

3.   16
      + 30

4.   16
      + 40

What numbers did you skip count on
the hundred chart to find the answers?   _____

Algebra

5. Fill in the missing digits to
complete the pattern.

5_____, 62, _____2, _____2

Adding Tens
on a Hundred Chart

1	2	3	4	5	6	7	8	9	10
11	12	13	14	15	16	17	18	19	20
21	22	23	24	25	26	27	28	29	30
31	32	33	34	35	36	37	38	39	40
41	42	43	44	45	46	47	48	49	50
51	52	53	54	55	56	57	58	59	60
61	62	63	64	65	66	67	68	69	70
71	72	73	74	75	76	77	78	79	80
81	82	83	84	85	86	87	88	89	90
91	92	93	94	95	96	97	98	99	100

Use the hundred chart to add tens.

1. 24 + 30 = _____   56 + 20 = _____   13 + 70 = _____

2. 11 + 80 = _____   67 + 10 = _____   39 + 40 = _____

Algebra

3. Which number sentence is equal
to 24 + 10?

○ 14 + 10   ○ 24 + 20

○ 14 + 20   ○ 34 + 10

Adding on a Hundred Chart

You can use a hundred chart to add two-digit numbers.

24 + 15

Start at 24.

Go down 1 row for every ten you add.

Go right 1 column for every one you add.

Because 15 is 1 ten and 5 ones, go down 1 row, and right 5 columns.

So, 24 + 15 = 39.

Row {

1	2	3	4	5	6	7	8	9	10
11	12	13	14	15	16	17	18	19	20
21	22	23	24	25	26	27	28	29	30
31	32	33	34	35	36	37	38	39	40
41	42	43	44	45	46	47	48	49	50
51	52	53	54	55	56	57	58	59	60
61	62	63	64	65	66	67	68	69	70
71	72	73	74	75	76	77	78	79	80
81	82	83	84	85	86	87	88	89	90
91	92	93	94	95	96	97	98	99	100

Column

Use the hundred chart. Follow the clues.
Write the missing number.

1. Start at 11.

11 + 15 = ?

Move down __1__ rows.   Move right __5__ columns.

11 + 15 = __26__

2. Start at 34.

34 + 64 = ?

Move down _____ rows.   Move right _____ columns.

34 + 64 = _____

Adding on a Hundred Chart

1	2	3	4	5	6	7	8	9	10
11	12	13	14	15	16	17	18	19	20
21	22	23	24	25	26	27	28	29	30
31	32	33	34	35	36	37	38	39	40
41	42	43	44	45	46	47	48	49	50
51	52	53	54	55	56	57	58	59	60
61	62	63	64	65	66	67	68	69	70
71	72	73	74	75	76	77	78	79	80
81	82	83	84	85	86	87	88	89	90
91	92	93	94	95	96	97	98	99	100

Use the hundred chart to add.

1. 51 + 24 = _____   45 + 33 = _____   38 + 61 = _____

2. 17 + 42 = _____   71 + 27 = _____   23 + 65 = _____

Reasoning

3. Which addition sentence matches the clues?

Start at 34.
Move down 4 rows.
Move right 2 columns.

○ 34 + 2 = 36   ○ 34 + 24 = 58

○ 34 + 4 = 38   ○ 34 + 42 = 76

Name_____

Adding Tens to Two-Digit Numbers

You can count on by tens to add.

3 tens

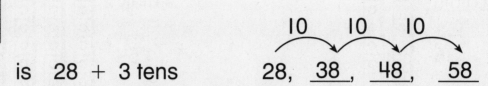

28 + 30   is   28 + 3 tens

28, _38_ , _48_ , _58_

28 + 30 = 58

Solve each number sentence.

1.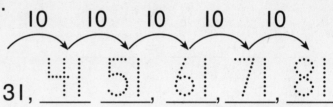

31, _41_ , _51_ , _61_ , _71_ , _81_

31 + 50 is 31 + __5__ tens

31 + 50 = _81_

2.

52 + 20 is 52 + _____ tens

52 + 20 = _____

52, _____ , _____

3.

33, _____ , _____ , _____ , _____

33 + 40 is 33 + _____ tens

33 + 40 = _____

Adding Tens to Two-Digit Numbers

Write each number sentence.

1. Think

36

_____ + _____ = _____

2. Think

54

_____ + _____ = _____

3. Think

63

_____ + _____ = _____

4. Think

47

_____ + _____ = _____

Number Sense

5. Will has 24 crayons.

He gets 4 more boxes of crayons.

Each box has 10 crayons.

How many crayons does Will have now?

64   54   44   34
○   ○   ○   ○

Adding to a Two-Digit Number

Add 26 and 5.

Show 26.   Add 5.

Regroup 10 ones as I ten.

Tens	Ones

Tens	Ones

Tens	Ones

Tens	Ones

$26 + 5 = \underline{31}$

Find the sum.

1. Add 16 and 7.

Show 16.   Add 7.   Regroup.   Find the sum.

Decenas	Unidades

Tens	Ones

Tens	Ones

Tens	Ones

$16 + 7 = \underline{23}$

2. Add 28 and 5.

Show 28.   Add 5.   Regroup.   Find the sum.

Tens	Ones

Tens	Ones

Tens	Ones

Tens	Ones

$28 + 5 = \underline{}$

Adding to a Two-Digit Number

Write the sum.

Find the sum.	**Do you need to regroup?**

1. $27 + 6 =$ ___33___   (yes)   no

2. $43 + 5 =$ _____   yes   no

3. $34 + 8 =$ _____   yes   no

4. $17 + 4 =$ _____   yes   no

5. $56 + 3 =$ _____   yes   no

6. $93 + 2 =$ _____   yes   no

7. $87 + 7 =$ _____   yes   no

8. $68 + 5 =$ _____   yes   no

9. $36 + 3 =$ _____   yes   no

10. **Journal** There are 24 counters.
How many counters could you add
without having to regroup? Why?

_____

_____

_____

Subtracting Tens on a Hundred Chart

1	2	3	4	5	6	7	8	9	10
11	12	13	14	15	16	17	18	19	20
21	22	23	24	25	26	27	28	29	30
31	32	33	34	35	36	37	38	39	40
41	42	43	44	45	46	47	48	49	50
51	52	53	54	55	56	57	58	59	60
61	62	63	64	65	66	67	68	69	70
71	72	73	74	75	76	77	78	79	80
81	82	83	84	85	86	87	88	89	90
91	92	93	94	95	96	97	98	99	100

To subtract by tens, you can count back by tens on a hundred chart. Move up a row for each ten you subtract. All of the numbers will end in the same number.

$41 - 30 =$ _____

Count back by tens on the hundred chart to subtract.

1.
$$\begin{array}{r} 84 \\ -\ 60 \\ \hline \end{array}$$
24

2.
$$\begin{array}{r} 59 \\ -\ 10 \\ \hline \end{array}$$

3.
$$\begin{array}{r} 45 \\ -\ 30 \\ \hline \end{array}$$

4.
$$\begin{array}{r} 78 \\ -\ 40 \\ \hline \end{array}$$

What numbers did you skip count on
the hundred chart to find the answers? _____

Algebra

5. Fill in the missing digits to complete the pattern.

8_____, 72, _____2, _____2

Subtracting Tens on a Hundred Chart

1	2	3	4	5	6	7	8	9	10
11	12	13	14	15	16	17	18	19	20
21	22	23	24	25	26	27	28	29	30
31	32	33	34	35	36	37	38	39	40
41	42	43	44	45	46	47	48	49	50
51	52	53	54	55	56	57	58	59	60
61	62	63	64	65	66	67	68	69	70
71	72	73	74	75	76	77	78	79	80
81	82	83	84	85	86	87	88	89	90
91	92	93	94	95	96	97	98	99	100

Use the hundred chart to subtract tens.

1. $87 - 40 =$ _____ $53 - 30 =$ _____ $71 - 60 =$ _____

2. $98 - 10 =$ _____ $32 - 20 =$ _____ $83 - 50 =$ _____

3. $43 - 20 =$ _____ $71 - 50 =$ _____ $66 - 40 =$ _____

Algebra

4. Which number completes the subtraction sentence?

$75 -$ _____ $= 35$

  ○ 20   ○ 40

  ○ 30   ○ 50

Name_____

Subtracting Tens from Two-Digit Numbers

You can count back by tens to subtract.

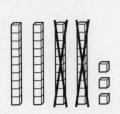

2 tens

10   10

43, __33__, __23__

43 − 20   is   43 − 2 tens

43 − 20 = __23__

Solve each number sentence.

1.
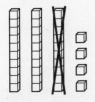

10

34, __24__

34 − 10   is   34 − __1__ ten

34 − 10 = __24__

2.
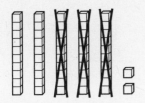

10

52, _____, _____, _____

52 − 30   is   52 − _____ tens

52 − 30 = _____

3.
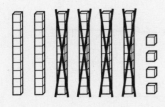

64, _____, _____, _____, _____

64 − 40   is   64 − _____ tens

64 − 40 = _____

Subtracting Tens from Two-Digit Numbers

Cross out the tens. Write the difference.

1.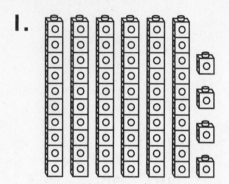

$64 - 20 = $ _____

2.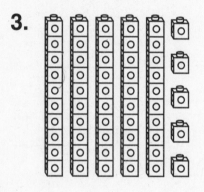

$47 - 30 = $ _____

3.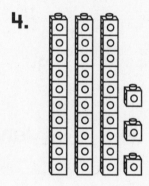

$55 - 40 = $ _____

4.

$33 - 10 = $ _____

Journal

5. Roberto says that $75 - 30 = 35$.
   Is Roberto correct?
   Explain.

_____

_____

Name_____

Subtracting from a Two-Digit Number

Find the difference for the problem 32 – 6.

Show 32.

Tens	Ones

Regroup 1 ten as 10 ones.

Tens	Ones

Subtract.

Tens	Ones

Subtract 6.

$32 - 6 = \underline{26}$

1. Find the difference for the problem 46 – 8.

Show 46.

Tens	Ones

Regroup.

Tens	Ones

Subtract.

Tens	Ones

Subtract 8.

$46 - 8 = \underline{38}$

2. Find the difference for the problem 23 – 7.

Show 23.

Tens	Ones

Regroup.

Tens	Ones

Subtract.

Tens	Ones

Subtract 7.

$23 - 7 = \underline{}$

Subtracting from a Two-Digit Number

Write the difference.

Find the difference.   **Do you need to regroup?**

1. $42 - 6 =$ ___36___   yes   no

2. $37 - 5 =$ _____   yes   no

3. $62 - 4 =$ _____   yes   no

4. $58 - 9 =$ _____   yes   no

5. $24 - 7 =$ _____   yes   no

6. $77 - 6 =$ _____   yes   no

7. $85 - 8 =$ _____   yes   no

8. $93 - 3 =$ _____   yes   no

Spatial Thinking

9. Draw cubes to show the same number in both place value mats.

Tens	Ones		Tens	Ones

Problem Solving:
Extra Information

Sometimes a problem has information you do not need.
When you solve a problem, you need to find what information
you do and do not need.

Karl has 52 baseball cards.
~~He has 37 baseball stickers.~~
His mom gives him 26 more cards.
How many cards does he have in all?

Underline the information you need.
Cross out the information you do not need.
Then write a number sentence to solve.

52 + 26 = 78 baseball cards

Read the problem.
Cross out the information you do not need.
Then write a number sentence to solve.

1. ~~David helped his dad sort DVDs and CDs.~~
There were 38 new DVDs.
There were 21 used DVDs.
How many DVDs in all?

_____ + _____ = _____ DVDs

2. There are 42 pink roses
in the garden.
There are 18 yellow daisies.
There are 47 red roses.
How many roses are there?

_____ + _____ = _____ roses

Problem Solving: Extra Information

Cross out the extra information.
Write a number sentence to solve the problem.
You can use cubes or a hundred chart to help.

1. There are 16 boys on Milo's flag
football team.
In their first game, they scored 14 points.
In their second game, they scored 28 points.
How many points did the team score in all?

points

2. Ms. Patel teaches tap dance and ballet.
There are 9 girls in her tap class.
All the girls are 6 years old.
There are 7 girls in her ballet class.
How many girls are there in all?

girls

Reasoning

3. One tank of goldfish has 35 fish.
The other tank has 42 fish.
A goldfish can live for 15 years.
How many fish are in both tanks?
Which sentence is extra information?

○ One tank of goldfish
  has 35 fish.

○ A goldfish can live
  for 15 years.

○ The other tank has
  42 fish.

○ How many fish are in
  both tanks?

Step Up to Grade 2

Name _____

Number Words to Twenty

One ___1___   Eleven _____

Two ___2___   Twelve _____

Three _____   Thirteen _____

Four _____   Fourteen _____

Five _____   Fifteen _____

Six _____   Sixteen _____

Seven _____   Seventeen _____

Eight _____   Eighteen _____

Nine _____   Nineteen _____

Ten _____   Twenty _____

Materials: Two-color counters, 20 per child

1. Have children show one counter. Say the word "one" as a class while children point to the word. Then have the children write the number in the blank beside the word.

2. Have children add one more counter. Say the word "two" as a class while children point to math word. Then have children write the number in the blank beside the word.

3. Repeat for each number to twenty.

Number Words to Twenty (continued)

Match each word to the correct number.

1. twelve   9

2. eighteen   4

3. nine   12

4. fifteen   18

5. four   11

6. eight   15

7. nineteen   19

8. eleven   14

9. twenty   8

10. fourteen   20

Name _____

Numbers to 100 on the Number Line

I.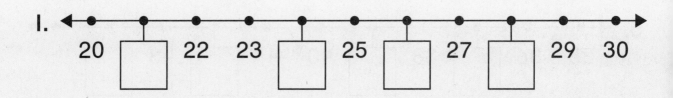

20　☐　22　23　☐　25　☐　27　☐　29　30

2.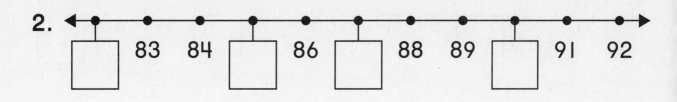

☐　83　84　☐　86　☐　88　89　☐　91　92

3.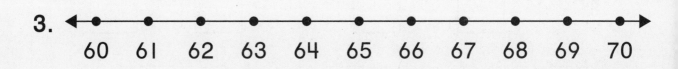

60　61　62　63　64　65　66　67　68　69　70

4.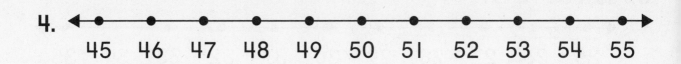

45　46　47　48　49　50　51　52　53　54　55

---

1. Say: *Every number has its own place on the number line. The numbers go in order from least to greatest. What number comes after 20?* Have children write 21 in the box.

2. *What number comes between 23 and 25?* Have children write 24 in the second box.

3. Have children complete the number lines for Problems 1 and 2. Ask questions like those above for children who have difficulty.

4. For Problem 3, have children find 64 on the number line and circle it and its point. Ask: *What number is before 64? After?* Have children circle 67 and its point. Ask: *Is 67 greater than or less than 64?*

5. Have children circle a number that is greater than 53 on the last number line. Then have them circle one that is less than 46.

Name _____

Numbers to 100 on the Number Line (continued)

Write the missing numbers.

5.

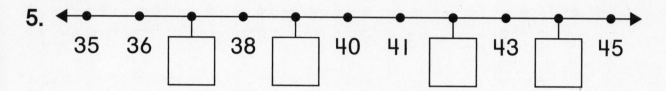

35   36   ☐   38   ☐   40   41   ☐   43   ☐   45

6.

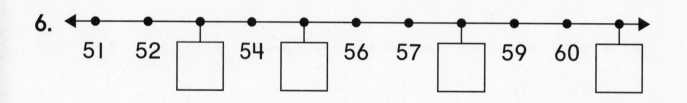

51   52   ☐   54   ☐   56   57   ☐   59   60   ☐

7.

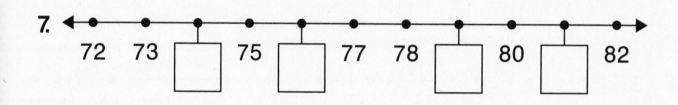

72   73   ☐   75   ☐   77   78   ☐   80   ☐   82

Circle the numbers on the number line.

8. 28, 33

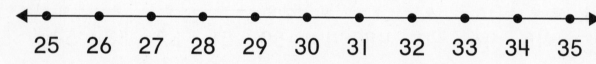

25   26   27   28   29   30   31   32   33   34   35

9. 91, 97

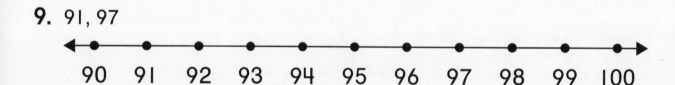

90   91   92   93   94   95   96   97   98   99   100

Name _____

Understanding One as a Fraction

1. 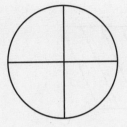   parts red

_____

parts in all _____ = 1

2. 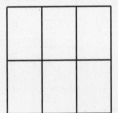 parts blue

_____

parts in all _____ = 1

3. 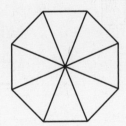 parts orange

_____

parts in all _____ = 1

4. parts yellow

_____

parts in all _____ = 1

5. **Reasoning** $\dfrac{\square}{9} = 1$

Materials: Crayons or markers

1. Have children color all 4 parts of the circle red. Ask: *How many parts are red?* Have children write 4. *How many parts in all?* Have children write 4 again. *What fraction of the circle is red?* Say: *Four fourths are red.*

2. Ask: *Is the whole circle red?* Say: *So, four fourths equal one whole.* Have children write $\frac{4}{4}$.

3. Have children color all 3 parts of the square blue. Ask questions like those above.

4. Have children finish the other problems, coloring all 6 parts of the square orange and all 8 parts of the octagon yellow.

Understanding One as a Fraction (continued)

Color each shape. Write a fraction equal to 1.

6. 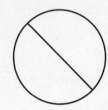   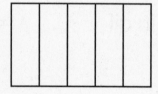 = 1

7.

_____ = 1

8.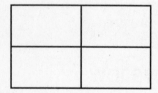

_____ = 1

9.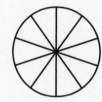

_____ = 1

10.

_____ = 1

11.

_____ = 1

12. Reasoning Color the whole group.

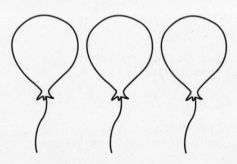   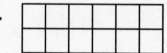 = 1

Name _____

Comparing Sets of Coins

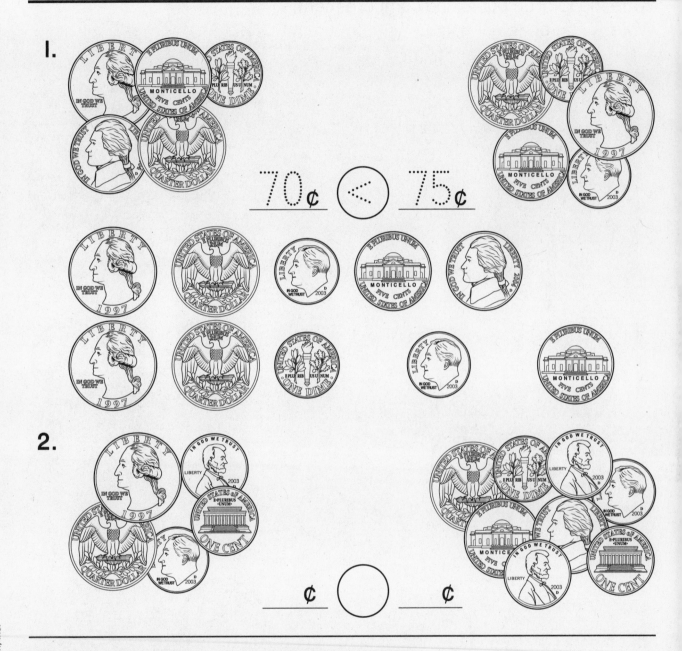

1.

70¢ < 75¢

2.

_____¢ ◯ _____¢

Materials: 3 quarters, 5 dimes, 3 nickels, and 3 pennies per child or pair.

1. Have children use the coins to match the ones in the first group. Have them arrange the coins, count on, and write the total value.

2. Have children line up the two groups of coins as shown. Have them cross out the first quarter in each group because they have the same value. Have them continue to cross out coins with the same value, 2 quarters, 2 dimes, and then 2 nickels and the dime. Since the second group of coins has a nickel left, it is greater than the first set. That means and the first set is less than the second. Have children write <.

3. Point out that 70 cents is less than 75 cents, since 70 is less than 75.

4. Repeat for the second group of coins. Tell children to not use coins from their first group.

5. Have children find the value of each set of coins in item 2 and compare.

Comparing Sets of Coins (continued)

Write the total amounts and compare them.
Write <, >, or =.

3.

48¢ ⊃ 43¢

4.

_____ ¢ ◯ _____ ¢

5.

_____ ¢ ◯ _____ ¢

Name _____

Ordering Numbers to 999

1.

132   223   124

<u>124</u>   <   <u>132</u>   <   <u>223</u>
least   greatest

2. | 213 | 141 | 236 | _____ < _____ < _____
least   greatest

3. | 436 | 487 | 243 | _____ < _____ < _____
least   greatest

4. | 431 | 283 | 281 | _____ < _____ < _____
least   greatest

Materials: Place value blocks, 10 hundreds, 8 tens, 10 ones per pair or group

1. Have children show 132, 223, and 124 with blocks.

2. Ask: *Which number has the greatest number of hundreds?* 223 Say: *If one number has more hundreds than all the others, it is the greatest.* Have children write 223 on the line with greatest.

3. Ask: *Does one number have the fewest number of hundreds?* No, 132 and 124 have the same number of hundreds. Say: *When two or more numbers have the same number of hundreds, compare the tens. Which number has fewer tens, 132 or 124?* 124 Say: *So, 124 is the least.* Have children write 124 on the line with least.

4. Ask: *Which number is between 124 and 223?* Have children write 132.

5. Say: *So the numbers in order from least to greatest are: 124, 132, 223.*

6. Have children order the other sets of numbers, using place value blocks, if they wish.

Name _____

Ordering Numbers to 999 (continued)

Write the numbers in order from **least** to **greatest**.

5. | 188 | 128 | 243 | 128 < 188 < 243
                        least   greatest

6. | 465 | 323 | 512 | ___ < ___ < ___
                        least   greatest

7. | 342 | 215 | 251 | ___ < ___ < ___
                        least   greatest

8. | 767 | 876 | 676 | ___ < ___ < ___
                        least   greatest

9. | 809 | 783 | 784 | ___ < ___ < ___
                        least   greatest

10. | 645 | 154 | 646 | ___ < ___ < ___
                        least   greatest

11. **Reasoning** The Lions have 117 points,
the Cougars have 112 points, and the
Tigers have 121 points. Which team has
the least number of points?   _____

Using Doubles to Subtract

1.

   $3 + 3 = \underline{6}$ So $6 - 3 = \underline{3}$.

2.

   $4 + 4 = \underline{\hspace{1cm}}$ So $8 - 4 = \underline{\hspace{1cm}}$.

3.

   $6 + 6 = \underline{\hspace{1cm}}$ So $12 - 6 = \underline{\hspace{1cm}}$.

4. $\underline{\hspace{1cm}} + \underline{\hspace{1cm}} = \underline{\hspace{1cm}}$

   $4 \quad - \quad 2 \quad = \underline{\hspace{1cm}}$

Materials: Snap cubes, 12 for each child

1. Have children make 2 trains of 3 snap cubes each. Ask: *How much is 3 plus 3?* Have children write 6. Have children break the train apart into two trains with 3 each. Ask: *Since 3 plus 3 is 6, what is 6 minus 3?* Have children write 3.

2. Say: *If you know the doubles addition facts, you can use them to subtract.* Have children use cubes to find 8 − 4 and 12 − 6.

3. Ask: *What doubles addition fact can you use to find 4 minus 2?* Have children complete 2 + 2 = 4. Ask: *What is 4 minus 2?* Have children write 2.

Name _____

Using Doubles to Subtract (continued)

Find the double. Then subtract.
Use cubes if you like.

5.

$$2 + 2 = \underline{\hspace{2cm}}$$

$$\text{So } 4 - 2 = \underline{\hspace{2cm}}.$$

6.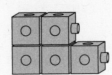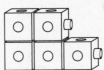

$$5 + 5 = \underline{\hspace{2cm}}$$

$$\text{So } 10 - 5 = \underline{\hspace{2cm}}.$$

Write an addition fact. Then subtract.

7. $1 + 1 = \underline{\hspace{2cm}}$ So $2 - 1 = \underline{\hspace{2cm}}.$

8. $3 + 3 = \underline{\hspace{2cm}}$ So $6 - 3 = \underline{\hspace{2cm}}.$

9. $4 + 4 = \underline{\hspace{2cm}}$ So $8 - 4 = \underline{\hspace{2cm}}.$

10. $\underline{\hspace{2cm}} + \underline{\hspace{2cm}} = 12$ So $12 - 6 = \underline{\hspace{2cm}}.$

11. Carolyn has 6 apples and 3 oranges.
How many pieces of fruit does she have in all?

_____ pieces of fruit

Stories about Separating

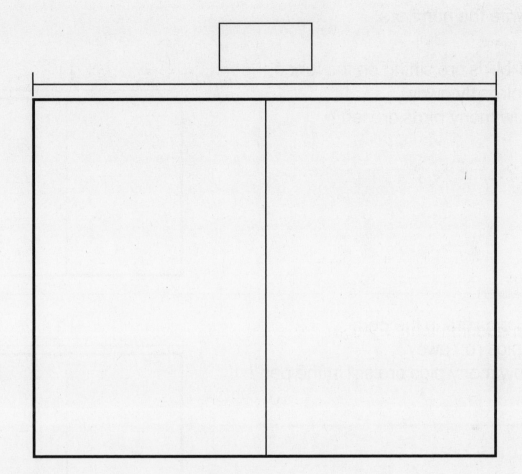

1. _12_ – _3_ = _9_   **2.** _____ – _____ = _____

3. _____ – _____ = _____   **4.** _____ – _____ = _____

Materials: Counters, 18 for each child

1. Say: *Rosa had 12 balloons.* Have children put 12 counters in the first box and write 12 in the first line of the number sentence. Say: *Rosa gave her sister 3 balloons.* Have children move 3 counters to the second box and write 3. Ask: *How many balloons did Rosa have then?* Have children count how many counters are left in the first box and write 9.

2. Say: *Quaid had 15 marbles.* Have children put 15 counters in the first box and write 15. Say: *Quaid gave his brother 7 marbles.* Have children move 7 counters to the second box and write 7. Ask: *How many marbles did Quaid have then?* Have children count how many counters are left in the first box and write 8.

3. Say: *What if Rosa had 18 balloons and gave away 9? How many balloons would Rosa have then?* Have children write a number sentence and use counters to solve.

4. Say: *What if Quaid had 13 marbles and gave 6 away? How many marbles would Quaid have then?* Have children write a number sentence and use counters to solve.

Stories about Separating (continued)

Draw a picture to find the difference.
Then write the numbers.

5. 11 birds are sitting on the fence.
7 birds fly away.
How many birds are left?

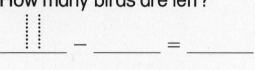

_____ − _____ = _____

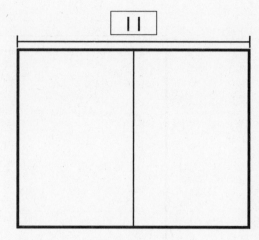

11

6. 13 pigs are in the pen.
5 pigs run away.
How many pigs are still in the pen?

_____ − _____ = _____

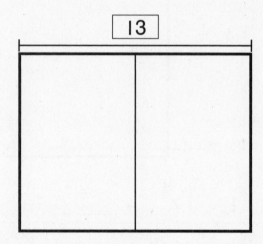

13

7. 16 ducks are in the pond.
9 ducks swim away.
How many ducks are left?

_____ − _____ = _____

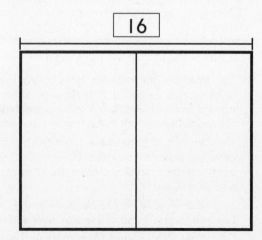

16

Stories about Comparing

1. _12_ – _5_ = _7_   _7_ more crayons

2. _____ – _____ = _____   _____ more grapes

3. _____ – _____ = _____   _____ more apples

4. _____ – _____ = _____   _____ more fish

5. _____ – _____ = _____   _____ more hair bows

Materials: Counters, 18 for each child

1. Say: *Alicia had 12 crayons.* Have children show 12 counters in a row and write 12. Say: *Max had 5 crayons.* Have children show 5 counters in a row below Alicia's and write 5. Say: *How many more crayons did Alicia have than Max?* Have children remove 1 counter from each row at the same time. Have them continue removing pairs until all the counters in the bottom row are gone. Have children complete the number sentence by writing 7.

2. Say: *Jaden had 16 grapes.* Have children show 16 counters in a row and write 16. Say: *Rafel had 8 grapes.* Have children show 8 counters in a row below Jaden's and write 8. Say: *How many more grapes did Jaden have than Max?* Have children remove 1 counter from each row at the same time. Have them continue removing pairs until all the counters in the bottom row are gone. Have children complete the number sentence by writing 8.

3. Say: *Vero had 14 apples and 5 oranges. How many more apples than oranges did she have?* Have children use counters to write and solve the number sentence.

4. Say: *Miles had 15 fish. Olivia had 6 fish. How many more fish did Miles have than Olivia?* Have children use counters to write and solve the number sentence.

5. Say: *Poppy had 11 hair bows. Lora had 3 hair bows. How many more hair bows did Poppy have than Lora?* Have children use counters to write and solve the number sentence.

Name _____

Stories about Comparing (continued)

Draw a picture to find the differences.
Then write a subtraction sentence.

6. 11 dogs are in a pen.
5 dogs are chasing a
cat. How many more
dogs are in the pen?

_____ more dogs   11 − 5 = _____

7. Paul has 14 dimes. Sue
has 6 dimes. How many
more dimes does Paul
have than Sue?

_____ more dimes   _____ − _____ = _____

8. 17 apples are in a basket.
8 apples are on the
ground. How many more
apples are in the basket?

_____ more apples   _____ − _____ = _____

Name _____

Arrays and Multiplication

Materials 16 counters per student

1. Show an array of 4 rows with 2 counters in each row.

2. Write a multiplication sentence for the array.

   _____ × _____ = _____
     Number   Number of   Total
     of Rows   Counters in Number of
               Each Row   Counters

3. How many counters are in the array? _____

4. Show an array of 2 rows with 4 counters in each row.

5. Write a multiplication sentence for this array.

   _____ × _____ = _____
     Number   Number of   Total
     of Rows   Counters in Number of
               Each Row   Counters

6. How many counters are in this array? _____

7. Both arrays have 8 counters.

   So, $4 \times 2 = 2 \times$ _____

8. Since both arrays have 8 counters then you can say,

   $4 \times 2 = 8$, and $2 \times 4 =$ _____

Knowing one multiplication fact means you know another.

9. If you know $3 \times 8 = 24$, then you know $8 \times 3 =$ _____ .

Arrays and Multiplication (continued)

Write a multiplication sentence for each array.

10.

11.

_____   _____

Draw an array to find each multiplication fact. Write the product.

12. $3 \times 5 =$ _____   **13.** $2 \times 6 =$ _____

Fill in the blanks.

14. $4 \times 8 = 32$, so $8 \times 4 =$ _____   **15.** $9 \times 2 = 18$, so _____ $\times 9 = 18$

16. $5 \times 7 = 35$, so $7 \times$ _____ $= 35$ **17.** $3 \times 6 = 18$, so _____ $\times 3 = 18$

18. $2 \times 4 = 8$, so $4 \times$ _____ $= 8$ **19.** $1 \times 6 = 6$, so $6 \times 1 =$ _____

20. Reasoning How does an array show equal groups?

Multiplying by 2 and 5

1. Continue skip counting by 2s on the number line below.

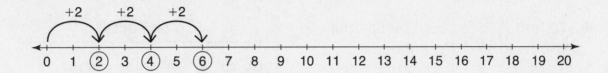

2. Each number that a hop lands on is a **multiple** of two. Circle each multiple of 2 on the number line. Then list them in the blanks below.

_____ _____ _____ _____ _____ _____ _____ _____ _____ _____

3. To find 6 × 2, count by 2s until you have said 6 numbers.

2, 4, _____, _____, 10, _____

So, 6 × 2 = _____.

4. Repeat 3 above for each of the 2s facts in the table. Complete the table.

2s Facts

$0 \times 2 = 0$	$5 \times 2 = $ _____
$1 \times 2 = $ _____	$6 \times 2 = 12$
$2 \times 2 = $ _____	$7 \times 2 = $ _____
$3 \times 2 = $ _____	$8 \times 2 = $ _____
$4 \times 2 = $ _____	$9 \times 2 = $ _____

5. Reasoning What is the pattern in the products of the 2s facts?

All of the multiples of 2 end in 0, 2, _____, _____, or _____.

6. Continue skip counting by 5s on the number line below. Circle each multiple of 5 on the number line.

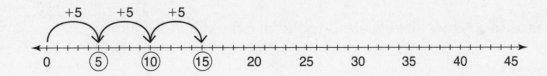

Name _____

Multiplying by 2 and 5 (continued)

7. Circle each multiple of 5 on the number line. Then list them in the blanks below.

_____ _____ _____ _____ _____ _____ _____ _____ _____

8. To find 7×5, count by 5s until you have said 7 numbers.

5, 10, 15, _____, _____,

_____, _____

So, $7 \times 5 =$ _____.

5s Facts

$0 \times 5 = 0$	$5 \times 5 =$ _____
$1 \times 5 =$ _____	$6 \times 5 =$ _____
$2 \times 5 =$ _____	$7 \times 5 = 35$
$3 \times 5 =$ _____	$8 \times 5 =$ _____
$4 \times 5 =$ _____	$9 \times 5 =$ _____

9. Repeat 8 above for each of the 5s facts in the table.

10. Reasoning What is the pattern in the products of the 5s facts?

All of the multiples of 5 end in _____ or _____.

Complete each multiplication problem.

11. $\begin{array}{r} 2 \\ \times\ 3 \\ \hline \end{array}$

12. $\begin{array}{r} 2 \\ \times\ 6 \\ \hline \end{array}$

13. $\begin{array}{r} 2 \\ \times\ 2 \\ \hline \end{array}$

14. $\begin{array}{r} 2 \\ \times\ 1 \\ \hline \end{array}$

15. $\begin{array}{r} 7 \\ \times\ 2 \\ \hline \end{array}$

16. $\begin{array}{r} 7 \\ \times\ 5 \\ \hline \end{array}$

17. $\begin{array}{r} 5 \\ \times\ 3 \\ \hline \end{array}$

18. $\begin{array}{r} 8 \\ \times\ 5 \\ \hline \end{array}$

19. $\begin{array}{r} 5 \\ \times\ 4 \\ \hline \end{array}$

20. $\begin{array}{r} 1 \\ \times\ 5 \\ \hline \end{array}$

21. $\begin{array}{r} 2 \\ \times\ 4 \\ \hline \end{array}$

22. $\begin{array}{r} 5 \\ \times\ 2 \\ \hline \end{array}$

23. Reasoning Movie tickets are on sale for $5 each. Ross, Emily, and John want to see the movie. Is $18 enough for all of their tickets? Explain.

Adding Two-Digit and One-Digit Numbers

1.

Tens	Ones
2	6
+	8

Tens	Ones
2	6
+	8
	4

Tens	Ones
1 2	6
+	8
3	4

2.

Tens	Ones
2	3
+	4

Tens	Ones
2	3
+	4

Tens	Ones
2	3
+	4
	7

3.

Tens	Ones
1	9
+	7

Tens	Ones
1	9
+	7

Tens	Ones
1 1	9
+	7
	6

Materials: Snap cubes, 34 per pair or group

1. Have children show two 10-trains and six individual cubes for 26. Then have them show 8 individual cubes. Ask: *How much is 6 ones and 8 ones?* 14 ones *If you have 14 ones can you regroup?* Have children snap together 10 ones to make 1 ten-train. Ask: *The 14 ones equal how many tens and ones?* 1 ten and 4 ones; Have children write a 4 in the bottom of the ones column of the second place-value chart, to show 4 ones, and a 1 in the box at the top of the tens column to show 1 ten. Say: *Add the tens. How much is 2 tens plus 1 ten?* Have children write the 3 in the tens column of the last place-value chart. Ask: *How much is 3 tens and 4 ones?* 34 *So, 26 + 8 = 34.*

2. Have children show two 10-trains and three individual cubes for 23. Then have them show four individual cubes. Ask: *How much is 3 ones and 4 ones?* 7 ones *If you have 7 ones can you regroup?* No; Have children write the 7 at the bottom of the ones column of the second place-value chart. Ask: *How many tens?* 2; Have children write a 2 in the tens column of the last place-value chart. Ask: *How much is 2 tens and 7 ones?* 27 *So, 23 + 4 = 27.*

3. Do Problem 3 similar to Problem 1.

Name _____

Adding Two-Digit and One-Digit Numbers (continued)

Add.
Regroup if you need to.

4.

Tens	Ones
☐	
2	3
+	8
3	

Tens	Ones
☐	
3	5
+	7

Tens	Ones
☐	
1	6
+	3

Tens	Ones
☐	
4	2
+	9

5.

Tens	Ones
☐	
3	5
+	5

Tens	Ones
☐	
7	2
+	6

Tens	Ones
☐	
2	3
+	7

Tens	Ones
☐	
4	2
+	9

6.

Tens	Ones
☐	
6	6
+	6

Tens	Ones
☐	
5	4
+	5

Tens	Ones
☐	
4	1
+	6

Tens	Ones
☐	
3	8
+	7

7.

Tens	Ones
☐	
9	2
+	3

Tens	Ones
☐	
1	4
+	4

Tens	Ones
☐	
3	9
+	9

Tens	Ones
☐	
6	4
+	6

Name _____

Subtracting Tens

1.

$7 \text{ tens} - 5 \text{ tens} = \underline{2} \text{ tens}$

$\underline{70} - \underline{50} = \underline{20}$

2.

$7 \text{ tens} - 2 \text{ tens} = \underline{5} \text{ tens}$

$\underline{} - \underline{} = \underline{}$

3.

$6 \text{ tens} - 2 \text{ tens} = \underline{} \text{ tens}$

$\underline{} - \underline{} = \underline{}$

Materials: Snap cubes, 70 for each pair or group

1. Have children make seven 10-trains. Then have them take five of the 10-trains away and cross out 5 of
the ten-trains shown. Ask: *Seven tens minus five tens equal how many tens?* Have children write 2.
Ask: *How much is 7 tens?* Have children write 70. Ask: *How much is 5 tens?* Have children write 50.
Ask: *How much is 2 tens?* Have children write 20. Say: *So, 70 − 50 = 20.*

2. Do the other problems similarly.

Name _____

Subtracting Tens (continued)

Write the numbers. Subtract.

4.

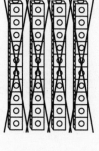

___6___ tens − ___1___ ten

___60___ − ___10___ = ___50___

5.

_____ tens − _____ tens

_____ − _____ = _____

6.

_____ tens − _____ tens

_____ − _____ = _____

7.

_____ tens − _____ tens

_____ − _____ = _____

8.

_____ tens − _____ tens

_____ − _____ = _____

9.

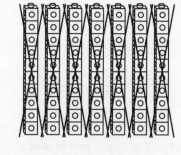

_____ tens − _____ tens

_____ − _____ = _____

Name _____

Finding Parts of 100

1.

55, _____, _____, _____, _____, _____, _____, _____, _____, _____

55 + _____ = 100

2.

55, _____, _____, _____, _____, _____, _____, _____, _____, _____

55 + _____ = 100

Materials: Snap cubes, 100 for each pair or group

1. Have children show five 10-trains and one 5-train of cubes. Ask: *How can you find out how many more snap cubes it will take to make 100?* Give children time to discuss possible ways. Say: *One way is to add ones until you make the next ten. Then count by tens until you get to 100. Start with 55 and add one snap cube at a time until you reach a ten.* Have the children add a snap cube to the 5-train, say 56, and write 56. Have them do this until they reach 60. Say: *Now count by tens.* Have the children add a 10-train down to the pile, say 70, and write 70. Do this until they reach 100. Say: *You added 5 ones and 4 tens. How much is 5 ones and 4 tens?* Have children write 45. Say: *So you had to add 45 to 55 to get 100. 55 + 45 = 100.*

2. Have children show five 10-trains and one 5-train of cubes again. Say: *Another way is to add tens first and then add ones. Start with 55 and add tens until you reach either 100 or a number in the 90s.* Have the children add a 10-train to the pile, say 65, and write 65. Have them do this until they reach 95. Say: *Now count by ones until you reach 100.* Have children add a snap cube to the 5-train, say 96, and write 96. Do this until they reach 100. Say: *You added 4 tens and 5 ones. How much is 4 tens and 5 ones?* Have children write 45.

3. Ask: *Does it matter if you count by ones first or tens first?* No

Finding Parts of 100 (continued)

Add on to find the other part of 100.
Use mental math or cubes.

3.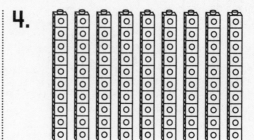

25 + __75__ = 100

4.

90 + _____ = 100

5.

33 + _____ = 100

6.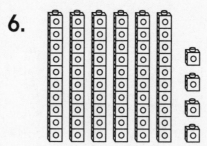

64 + _____ = 100

7. 37 + _____ = 100

8. 85 + _____ = 100

9. 56 + _____ = 100

10. 71 + _____ = 100

11. Reasoning The lunchroom holds 100 children.
There are 60 children eating in the lunchroom.
How many more can join them?

_____ + _____ = 100   _____ children

© Pearson Education, Inc.

Name ______________________________

Two-Digit Subtraction

1.

	Tens	Ones
	6	16
	~~7~~	~~6~~
−	2	8
	4	8

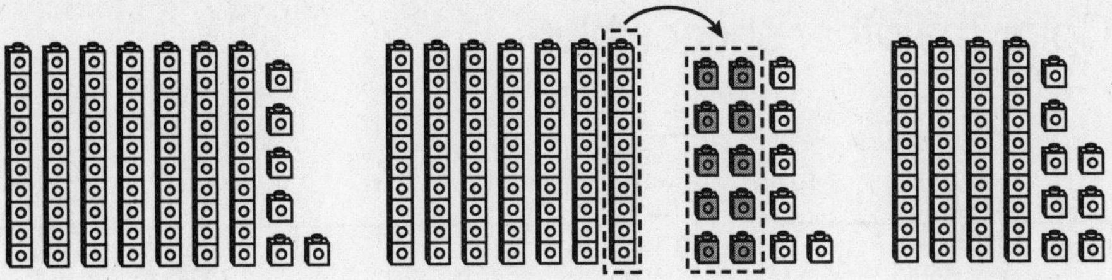

2.

	Tens	Ones
	9	4
−	2	2

	Tens	Ones
	6	7
−	1	9

	Tens	Ones
	3	0
−	1	3

	Tens	Ones
	8	2
−	5	5

3.

91	38	63	56	55	13
− 73	− 19	− 36	− 28	− 20	− 5

Materials: Have snap cubes available for children who need them

1. Ask: ***How many ones are in 76?*** 6 ***How many ones are in 28?*** 8 ***Does 76 have 8 ones to take away?*** No ***Do you need to regroup?*** Yes ***How many tens are in 76?*** 7 ***If you trade one ten for ten ones, how many tens are left?*** 6 tens ***Show this by crossing out the 7 tens in the place-value chart and writing 6 at the top of the tens column.*** Make sure children record correctly. ***You had 6 ones and traded one ten for ten ones. How many ones do you have now?*** 16 ***Show this by crossing out the 6 ones and writing 16 at the top of the ones column.*** Make sure children record correctly.
2. Ask: ***How much is 16 ones minus 8 ones?*** Have children write 8 in the ones column. Ask: ***How much is 6 tens minus 2 ten?*** Have children write 4 in the tens column. Say: ***How much is 4 tens and 8 ones?*** 48 ***So, 76 minus 28 is 48.***
3. Do other problems, similarly. When you get to 91 − 73, which is not in a place-value chart, start by asking how many tens and ones are in each number.

Two-Digit Subtraction (continued)

Subtract. Regroup if you need to.
If you had to regroup, color those shapes red.
Color the other shapes blue.

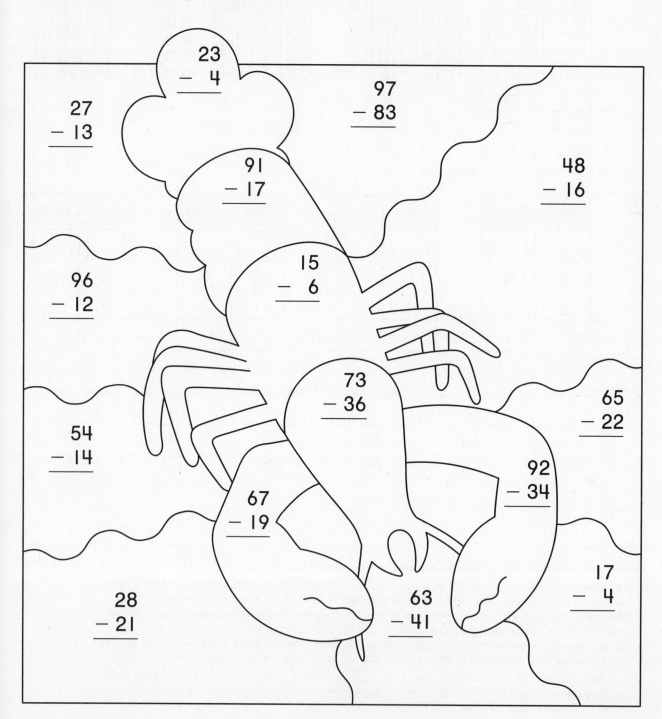

Name _____

Estimating Differences

When Jarvis subtracted 41 − 29, he got a difference of 12.
To check that this answer is reasonable, use estimation.

1. Round each number to the nearest ten.

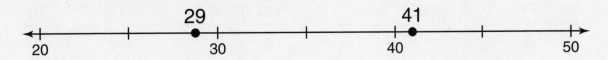

41 rounded to the nearest ten is _____ .

29 rounded to the nearest ten is _____ .

2. Subtract the rounded numbers.

40 − 30 = _____

Since 12 is close to 10, the answer is reasonable.

DaNitra subtracted 685 − 279 and got a difference of 406.
To check that this answer is reasonable, use estimation.

3. Round each number to the nearest hundred.

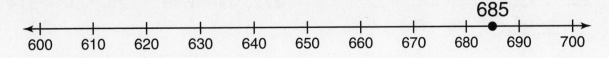

685 rounded to the nearest hundred is _____ .

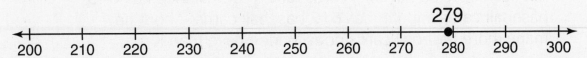

279 rounded to the nearest hundred is _____ .

4. Subtract the rounded numbers.

700 − 300 = _____

Since 406 is close to 400, the answer is reasonable.

Estimating Differences (continued)

Estimate by rounding to the nearest ten.

5.   47
     − 19

6.   82
     − 34

7. 67 − 51 _____

8. 94 − 48 _____

9.   71
     − 12

10.   65
      − 49

11. 89 − 24 _____

12. 51 − 38 _____

13.   93
      − 45

14.   88
      − 32

15. 57 − 18 _____

16. 28 − 17 _____

Estimate by rounding to the nearest hundred.

17.   586
      − 195

18.   941
      − 362

19. 442 − 181 _____

20. 861 − 298 _____

21.   418
      − 125

22.   546
      − 234

23. 945 − 119 _____

24 681 − 132 _____

25.   935
      − 464

26.   322
      − 176

27. 709 − 649 _____

28. 550 − 214 _____

29. Reasoning Marlee has collected baseball cards for 3 years. Kin has collected baseball cards for 2 years. Marlee has 845 baseball cards and Kin has 612 baseball cards. About how many more baseball cards does Marlee have than Kin? _____

30. Reasoning What is the smallest number that can be subtracted from 723 so that the difference is 200 when both numbers are rounded to the nearest hundred? Explain.

Name _____

Inches

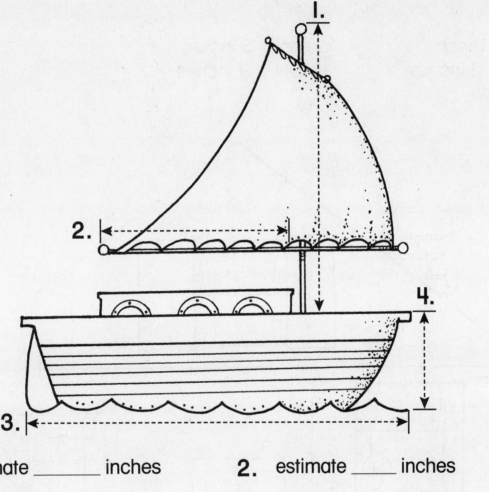

1. estimate _____ inches

measure _____ inches

2. estimate _____ inches

measure _____ inches

3. estimate _____ inches

measure _____ inches

4. estimate _____ inches

measure _____ inches

Materials: Inch rulers, 1 for each child

1. Show children an inch on a ruler. Ask them to find the line numbered 1 on the boat. Ask: *About how many inches long do you think the line is?* Have children write their estimates.

2. Draw a line on the board or overhead and demonstrate how to measure its length. Tell children to line up the zero on the ruler+ with one end of the line and read the number that is closest to the other end. Have children measure the line numbered one on the boat and write the measure.

3. Have children compare their measures to their estimates.

4. Have children estimate and then measure the other lines.

Name _____

Inches (continued)

Use a ruler. Measure each dotted line on the house.
Color the lines to show how long each line is.

red = 1 inch   green = 3 inches
blue = 2 inches   yellow = 4 inches

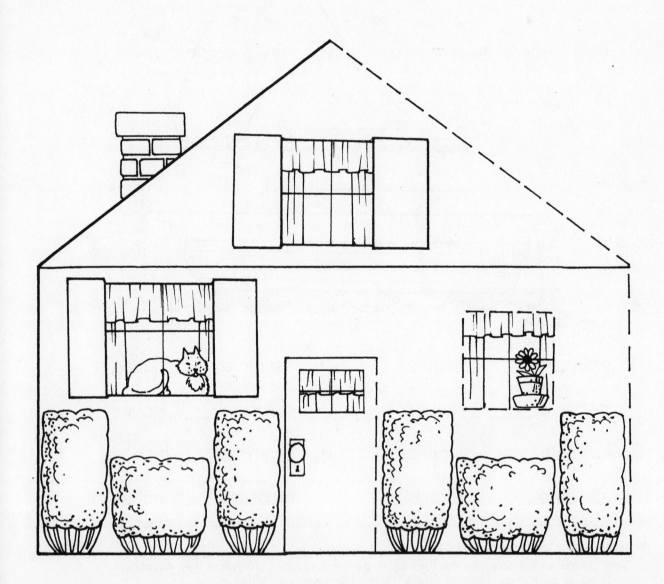

Centimeters and Meters

1. about 1 centimeter

2. about 1 meter

3.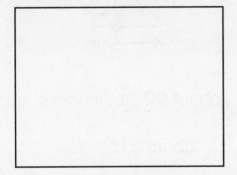

about _____ centimeters

4.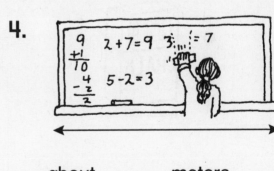

about _____ meters

Materials: meter stick and feather for demonstration

1. Show children one centimeter on the meter stick. Tell them a pencil is about one centimeter wide. Ask them to draw pictures in the first rectangle to show objects that are about one centimeter long or wide.

2. Tell children the meter stick is one meter long and a door is about one meter wide. Ask them to draw pictures in the second rectangle to show objects that are about one meter long or wide.

3. Show the feather. Ask: *Would you use centimeters or meters to measure the length of the feather?* centimeters *About how many centimeters long is the feather?* Have children write their estimates. Discuss the estimates.

4. Ask: *Would you use centimeters or meters to measure the length of the bulletin board?* meters *About how many meters long is the bulletin board?* Have children write their estimates. Discuss the estimates.

Name _____

Centimeters and Meters (continued)

About how long or tall might the real object be?
Circle the better estimate.

5.

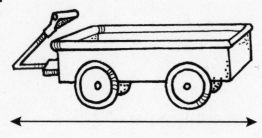

about I centimeter

about I meter

6.

about 30 centimeters

about 3 meters

7.

about 10 centimeters

about I meter

8.

about I centimeter

about I meter

9. Reasoning Would it take
more centimeters or meters
to measure your height?
Circle your answer.

centimeters

meters

Name _____

Flat Surfaces of Solid Figures

1.   ◯   ☐

2.   ◯   ☐

3.   ◯   ☐

4.   ◯   ☐

Materials: Cylinder, cube, sphere, and cone geometric solids

1. Show the cylinder and ask children its name. Ask: ***Does a cylinder have any flat surfaces?*** It has two.
   Ask: ***If you traced one of the flat surfaces, what shape would you get?*** Hold the cylinder against the board or overhead and trace around the bottom to make a circle. Have children ring the circle.

2. Repeat with the cube and the cone similarly.

3. Show the sphere. Ask: ***Does a sphere have any flat surfaces?*** no

Flat Surfaces of Solid Figures (continued)

Look at each shape.
Circle the object that has the flat surface.

5.

6.

7.

8.

9.

Name _____

Properties of Plane Shapes

1. Square

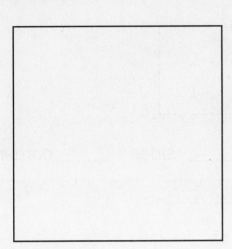

2. 3 corners

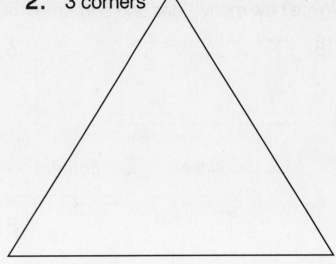

3. 0 corners

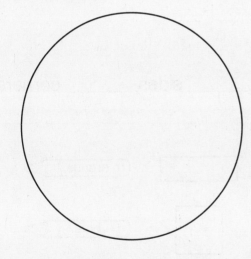

4. 6 sides

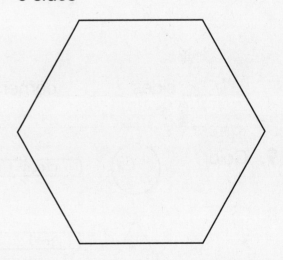

Materials: Attribute blocks, one triangle, one square, one rectangle, one circle, and one hexagon for each child or pair

1. Show a corner and a side of an attribute block. Have children touch one of each on a block.

2. Ask the children to choose the square and trace it in the first space on their paper. Ask: **How many sides does a square have?** Have children write 4 inside the square they drew. Ask: **How many corners does a square have?** Have children write 4 inside the square again.

3. Ask the children to choose the shape with 3 corners, trace it in the second space, and write the number of sides. Ask: **What is the name of the shape with 3 corners?** triangle

4. Ask the children to choose the shape with zero corners and trace it in the third space. Ask: **What is the name of the shape with 0 corners?** circle

5. **Reasoning** Ask the children to choose the shape with 6 sides, trace it in the last space, and write the number of corners.

Name _____

Properties of Plane Shapes (continued)

Trace each side in a different color.
Draw an X on each corner.
Write how many sides and corners.

5.
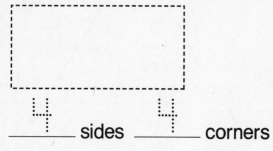
____4____ sides ____4____ corners

6.

_____ sides _____ corners

7.

_____ sides _____ corners

8.
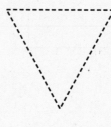
_____ sides _____ corners

9. Color

 green

 orange

 red

 blue

   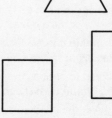 

Making Bar Graphs to Show Outcomes

Materials 3 index cards (cut in half vertically), bag

1. Write each letter in the word "MUMMY" on an index card. Use the extra index card to make a tally chart for the possible outcomes: M, U, and Y.

2. Place the letters in a bag. Shake them and without looking pick a letter. Tally the letter. Replace the letter, shake, pick, and tally. Do this 20 times.

Answer 3 to 8 to make and use a bar graph of the results.

3. Write the title: Letters Picked from Bag above the graph and label the axes: Outcome and Number of Times.

4. Complete the scale. Make the scale by 2s.

5. Draw a bar for each letter. For every 2 tally marks for the letter M, color in one square above the letter M. After coloring a square for every 2 tallies, if you have a tally left over, color half of a square. Do this for U and Y.

6. Which two letters were picked about the same number of times?

   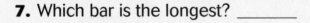

7. Which bar is the longest? _____

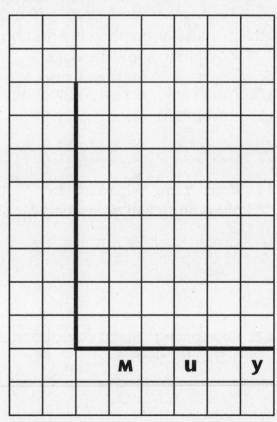

Since the bar above M is the longest, M is the outcome that occurred most often.

8. **Reasoning** Predict the next letter picked. Explain how you made your prediction.

Making Bar Graphs to Show Outcomes (continued)

Kendra spun a spinner 20 times. She recorded the number of times each color was spun. Use the data for Exercises 9 to 13.

Spinner Results		
Outcome	**Tally**	**Number**
Purple	~~IIII~~ ~~IIII~~ I	11
Green	IIII	4
Orange	IIII	4
Yellow	I	1

9. Make a bar graph in the grid on the right to show the data.

10. Which color occurred most often? least often?

_____

11. Reasoning What can you tell from the orange and green bars?

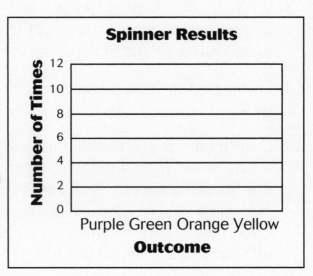

12. Reasoning Which color do you predict would be spun next?

_____

13. Reasoning Draw what you think the spinner looked like that Kendra used.

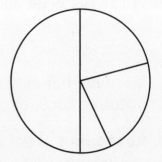